Culture and Climate Change: N

Edited by Joe Smith, Renata Tyszczuk
and Robert Butler

Published by Shed, Cambridge

Editors: Joe Smith, Renata Tyszczuk
and Robert Butler
Design by Hyperkit

ISBN 978-0-9557534-3-5

Printed by Lecturis, Eindhoven

This publication is printed on Munken Lynx
paper which is FSC accredited and produced
at a mill certified to the ISO 14001 and EMAS
environmental management standards. Printed
at Lecturis using eco-friendly BIO inks.

Contents

Acknowledgements 4

Introduction: What sort of story is climate change? 6

Six essays
Making a drama out of a crisis Robert Butler 11

From truth war to a game of risk Joe Smith 15

Greenland: How the National Theatre created a 25
climate change play Kellie C. Payne

What shall we tell the children? Alice Bell 37

Cautionary tales: The Sky is Falling! The World is Ending! 45
Renata Tyszczuk

Words after things: narrating the ends of worlds Bradon Smith 58

In Conversation 70
Nick Drake, Kate Fletcher, Caspar Henderson and Zoë Svendsen
talk with Joe Smith. With contributions from Feimatta Conteh,
Roger Harrabin, Alex Holland, Anna Jones, Charlie Kronick, Bridget
McKenzie, Lucy Neal, Daniel Nelson and Bradon Smith

Eleven Stories
Tan Copsey 90
Kris De Meyer 91
Isabel Hilton 92
Chris Hope 94
George Marshall 96
Ruth Padel 98
James Painter 99
Mike Shanahan 102
Marina Warner 104
Chris West 105
Barry Woods 107

Contributors 110
Bibliography 113
Timeline 117

Acknowledgements

We gratefully acknowledge the Ashden Trust and the Open University Open Space Research Centre for their continued support of the Mediating Change group, including its events, podcasts and this publication. Thanks are due to Sian Ferguson, Trust Executive at the Sainsbury Family Charitable Trusts, and Parvati Raghuram, Director, and Louise Topley, Administrator, both at Open Space.

The podcast and the transcript that appears in this volume are derived from an event held in partnership with Free Word: 'What Sort of Story is Climate Change?' Sam Sedgman at Free Word undertook the recording and editing of the podcast and Lauren Moody transcribed it. Thanks also to the staff supporting the events in other ways, particularly Executive Director Eleanor Lang.

The publication and related events have drawn on work funded through an Arts and Humanities Research Council (AHRC) development grant leading to the AHRC *Stories of Change* project. Renata Tyszczuk's work has been supported by a British Academy Mid-Career Fellowship (2013-2014).

This publication is integral to the 'Weatherfronts: Climate Change and the Stories We Tell' workshop being organised by Peter Gingold of TippingPoint and Rose Fenton of Free Word. The workshop is funded by Arts Council England and seeks to invite creative writers to engage with climate change. This volume provides a working document for that event.

We are particularly grateful to Hannah Bird, who produced the events and publication, and Eleanor Margolies, our copy-editor.

Joe, Renata and Robert

What Sort of Story is Climate Change?

Introduction

Climate change is understood to be urgent and important, and at the same time is widely seen as boring, difficult and confusing. It poses a global risk, and yet is highly divisive. It represents a defining challenge for our age, and yet it is one that many people choose to ignore and some, even, to deny.

In the two years leading up to the climate change negotiations in Copenhagen in 2009, there was an enormous amount of media attention around the subject. One storyline emerged as the dominant one: there was a universal threat, the science was 'settled', and the answer would have to be global policy responses that would affect many people's lives. But that storyline — which we might call 'the Gore narrative' — proved insufficiently supple and robust. The rapid journey that people were offered — from apocalyptic scenarios to low-energy lightbulbs — asked too much, too quickly, and many welcomed the chance, when it came along, to reject it.

How might other stories about climate change help to ensure a better quality of understanding, debate and action? The editors of this book believe that climate change requires multiple framings and perspectives, and that these need to be provisional and evolving. Only some voices have so far had the chance to speak and the stories that have been told represent only a fraction of the ones that might be available to us.

This book also tries to draw attention to the many ways in which climate change has a wider cultural significance, and deeper reach, than research and policy discourses generally tend to recognise. Climate change research is difficult new knowledge. It introduces complexities, anxieties and new questions into many areas of life.

In the past there has been a tendency for the research and policy community to treat the communication of climate change as a demanding but simple problem of 'getting the message across'. And in its accounts of the future this message has had a very limited narrative range, lurching rapidly between radical pessimism and techno-optimism. The big environmental NGOs have swung between these two poles, with chants of 'too little too late' alternating with somehow unconvincing promises of 'win—win' technical solutions. Within this confusing context, contrarian accounts that describe climate change as 'the greatest scientific hoax in history' have found ready listeners (particularly in the United States and Australia) who have been comforted by the idea that the science is at best uncertain, and that the policies proposed are damaging, politically-motivated, and anti-prosperity. The result is that politicians claim that they lack the political space for more decisive action.

This unstable public platform for action on climate change is in part explained by the arrival of a long and deep global recession. As with previous economic downturns, there has been a sharp falling away in the political importance of climate change and environmental concerns more broadly. Powerful economic and political interests, supported by mainstream news organisations, have been quick to fall back on the perceived successes of economic growth driven by fossil fuels, although it is important to note positive developments too. These include a sustained and spreading public concern, matched by genuine advances in business and social responses. Progress is often made through networks or within global institutions, including corporations and civil society. It should also be acknowledged that, despite all the criticisms of their pace, UN processes have often spurred social and business achievements in reducing emissions.

The conditions that are required for fuller public engagement with and debate about climate change are complex. This makes it an important time to think carefully about the stories that are told about climate change, and the politics of knowledge that surrounds it. In 2011 we published the first volume in this series, Culture and Climate Change: Recordings. The panel discussions and essays were informed by academic research but freed from scholarly conventions. This new volume of essays — and the associated event and podcast — seeks to reflect further on the kinds of stories that are already being told and to ask what new narratives about climate change might need to be nurtured.

The rapidly expanding body of artistic and cultural work that responds to climate change reflects a strong imaginative engagement across many disciplines. There is now a deeper and more diverse research base, including contributions from the humanities. Although the natural scientists have become increasingly confident of their headline messages it is also clear that it is wholly wrong to frame research into climate change as in any sense 'finished'. Transformations in the cultural sphere, above all in social and digital media, are having ambiguous, but potentially very constructive, consequences for the ways in which stories about climate change develop and travel. Among other things, these changes encourage more plural and dynamic accounts of our understanding of climate change and the actions that are available to us.

Our event at Free Word in December 2013 asked, 'What Sort of Story is Climate Change?' We have included an edited transcript of the contributions and discussion that followed. We put the same question to a mixture of contributors including a writer, a poet, researchers, journalists, a citizen blogger and a campaigner. The book also includes a series of longer essays which explore narratives of climate change from a range of perspectives and cultural forms including literature, theatre, children's media and design. Together they make space for a wider range of voices and stories about climate change. We hope they will invite and inform many more.

Joe Smith, Renata Tyszczuk and Robert Butler

Six essays

Making a drama out of a crisis

Robert Butler

Last year I went to the launch of a report titled 'The Environment on TV: Are Broadcasters Meeting The Challenge?' Its main focus was how British broadcasters have covered climate change — or, more accurately, not covered it. The report's author, Caroline Haydon, told the audience that the long-form TV documentary was the most effective way of interesting the public in a subject, but in the last 12 months there had not been a single long-form programme about climate change on British TV — a striking omission.

The panel discussion which followed revealed a remarkable gulf between the panellists. Professor Chris Rapley, a former director of the Science Museum, said that climate change was 'the greatest drama in human history'. How could it be, then, that TV broadcasters were running shy of this subject? But Ralph Lee, head of Factual at Channel Four, said that he didn't see that it was part of his job to tell the public about climate change. 'We don't make public information films. The worst thing you can do is broadcast bad news and say there's nothing you can do about it.' The way out of this impasse, it seemed, was through 'narratives'. Leo Hickman, former *Guardian* journalist and now chief advisor on climate change at the World Wildlife Fund, said: 'The one thing this report highlights is the word narratives. I almost have a daily conversation about investigating narratives.'

It was odd to hear, on the one hand, that climate change was 'the greatest drama in human history' and, on the other, that it wasn't the job of broadcasters to make programmes about it. There are other global events — war, famine, migration — that programme-makers deal with directly. Odder still, was to hear what they could agree on: 'better communication' about climate change, which in turn required more discussion about 'narratives'. It was as if the whole subject had to be quarantined first before anyone would approach it. No TV executive would say 'we can't make a programme about a famine or a war because we don't broadcast bad news when there's nothing the TV audience can do about it'. Or, 'we would make a programme about a famine or a war, but not until we have spent more time investigating narratives'. And what exactly were these 'narratives' that needed investigating? One of the frustrations of the launch was the way that words like 'narratives', 'stories' and 'drama' were being used, interchangeably, for quite contradictory ends.

There's an academic debate (among post-structuralists and others) about what distinguishes a 'story' from a 'narrative' but, for the purpose of this essay,

I am using 'story', 'narrative' and 'drama' almost synonymously. They each call on an intimate and imaginative engagement from the reader or audience member, and each contrasts markedly with the other forms of communication about climate change: official reports, statistics, polls, op-ed pieces, blogposts, campaign slogans, headlines, soundbites and tweets.

These other forms of communication are in the business of framing events as part of the political process. They say to the audience: 'Please see the world the way we see it and join our side of the debate'. As such, the thinking has largely been done before the act of communication itself takes place and what follows is the marketing of the idea. (Artists of any sort should steer clear: it's not the job of the artist to illustrate the arguments of a political party, oil company or NGO.) This type of 'story' — literal, reductive and short-termist — is not what I want to consider here. But it's helpful to keep in mind, when discussing the relationship between climate change and stories (and, even, 'What sort of story is climate change?'), that there are two very different kinds of storytelling going on. As the debate at Westminster made apparent, when these two are conflated, very little progress occurs.

To step back for a moment: the discovery of anthropogenic climate change represents a fundamental shift in how we view the world and our place in it. But there have, of course, been many other imaginative shifts of great magnitude. At the beginning of the sixteenth century, for instance, Copernicus developed the theory that the Sun didn't move around the Earth, the Earth moved round the Sun. We were just one more planet. Two centuries later, the earthquake that destroyed Lisbon (which took place when many of the city's inhabitants were in church) inspired Enlightenment writings by Kant, Rousseau and Voltaire that questioned the idea of a benevolent God. A century after that, the arguments put forward in Darwin's *Origin of Species* would ripple out, and be absorbed and contested in the novels of — among others — George Eliot and Thomas Hardy. Fifty years later, Einstein's Theory of Relativity paved the way for modernism in the arts. And another 50 years after that, on August 6th 1945, the dropping of an atom bomb over Hiroshima altered forever how a generation thought about its colossal power and vulnerability.

It's within this kind of framework then, of major shifts in our sense of ourselves, that we ought to consider the series of reports that have been issued by the Intergovernmental Panel on Climate Change. Over the last 25 years, and with increasing firmness, these reports have forced us to rethink the parameters of cause and effect, costs, personal responsibilities, the interdependence of countries, and the trade-off between our lives and future generations. The reports have ushered in a new chapter in the history of thought — it is now part of who we are — and, as such, the news that these reports have brought will play itself out over the coming decades in the themes of countless novels, plays, operas and songs.

When we call for more stories about climate change we are not asking for more coverage of climate change in the media. We are asking for more works of literature — writing of the highest order! — that examine, interpret and make sense of this new era. Not to rally us to a cause, or to encourage us to make adjustments in our lifestyle, but to deepen our understanding of a predicament that didn't exist a generation ago. We want writers who can explore its richness and complexity, its myriad points of view, its ironies and ambiguities, its horror and, of course, its humour. It was Robert F. Kennedy in the 60s who gave currency in the West to the supposed Chinese curse: 'May you live in interesting times'. We live in one now, and we need writers who can reflect that.

Those who might be tempted to look at the question 'what sort of story is climate change?' and search for a utilitarian answer — one that might help us meet targets and reduce emissions — should bear in mind a number of facts (or inconvenient truths).

A natural disaster isn't a story. The Lisbon earthquake was a devastating event. Voltaire's *Candide* is a satire. Soon after the eponymous hero Candide arrives in Lisbon with Dr Pangloss and a heartless sailor, an earthquake hits the city, followed by a tsunami, and then a fire. Voltaire tells us that 30,000 people were killed. But the three characters whose lives we are following going on behaving in characteristic ways: the sailor goes looting, Candide goes begging, and Pangloss delivers a lecture on optimism. Voltaire's interest lies in the human reactions that follow on from the earthquake.

It doesn't matter how big and scary the statistics are. As *Candide* shows, the most terrifying moments — earthquakes, tsunamis, fires — act as the backdrop against which individual stories unfold. There's no correlation between the newsworthiness of an event — its death toll, for instance — and its emotional impact. A bored French housewife, who likes pink ribbons and romantic novels, has an affair. How could that trivial incident be a more compelling story than the deaths of 30,000 people? In Flaubert's hands, it is.

Stories about climate change don't need to be about climate change. Stories written before people knew about human-made climate change — *Faust*, *Galileo*, *King Lear* — may now resonate in ways that hadn't been seen before. Even if climate change is not the subject matter, or the principal theme, its presence may still be detectable. It could be, in Ian McEwan's evocative phrase, 'the background hum'. Also, the subject of a story is not the same as its theme, and even its ostensible theme may not be its actual theme, which the author may have hidden early on, and only gradually choose to reveal. Cormac McCarthy's novel *The Road* has been described as the greatest novel about climate change, and he hung out with climate scientists before writing it. But it makes no reference to climate change.

A good story doesn't need to change a lightbulb. Most stories don't set out to achieve a particular end and, if they did, there would be very little data available to measure their effectiveness. And even if a story did have a particular design on the reader, we cannot predict that the reader will take from the story what the writer intended. If stories about climate change were to have an instrumental purpose we must assume that the story will be understood in the way that is intended (a big if) and that readers will act afterwards in the way that is consonant with the purpose of the story (an even bigger if).

People read against the grain. Chekhov's story 'The Darling' was much admired by Tolstoy. It depicts a woman who subsumes her identity into the lives of the men she is at one time or another married to, or lives with. Two years after Chekhov's death, Tolstoy organised for the story to be reprinted and wrote an afterword that gives his interpretation of 'The Darling'. 'Chekhov intended to curse,' he wrote, 'but the god of poetry commanded him to bless, and he unconsciously clothed this sweet creature in such exquisite radiance that she will always be a model of what a woman should be in order to be happy herself.' Tolstoy believed Chekhov's story confirmed his own anti-feminist position. It didn't. But if Russia's greatest novelist can miss the point...

If climate change is human-made, the stories will be about human nature. One of the most powerful themes in fiction is the way that people do not behave in their own best interests, from Lear's banishment of his youngest daughter for her candour to Emma Bovary's passion for the opportunistic Rodolphe. In its own way, Lear has something to say about climate change. Nature tames his hubris. And, in its own way, *Madame Bovary* has something to say about climate change. It charts, in all-too-believable detail, how — despite the warning signs — a person will risk everything. In telling this story, Flaubert provides the most beautiful example of a tipping point. Emma thinks that she has fallen suddenly, madly, in love. But the narrator takes another view. The narrator thinks that, for the bored housewife, the catastrophe has been a long time coming:

> Little did she know that up on the roof of the house, the rain will form a pool if the gutters are blocked, and there she would have stayed feeling safe inside, until one day she suddenly discovered the crack right down the wall.

From truth war to a game of risk

Joe Smith

Most people know about and are concerned about climate change, even if their understanding is limited. But a good portion are sceptical of the science or resulting policies, particularly in some high-polluting developed countries including the US, UK, Australia and Canada. The international politics, despite some real achievements, feels tired and unresolved. Some people have sought to eradicate doubt and unblock politics by waging a truth war in the media that will bring some kind of conclusive victory for the climate change 'consensus'. By contrast I want to propose that insisting ever more loudly on the truthfulness and dominance of a body of science whose main conclusions have not changed in nearly a quarter of a century may only serve to further entrench oppositions. Here I want to argue for a very different approach which might invite a different kind of engagement with climate research and a more lively and convincing climate politics.

My essay in *Culture and Climate Change: Recordings* (2011) explored the novelty of the cultural politics surrounding climate change, and plotted six often inter-relating features. These include: its global pervasiveness; its far-reaching uncertainties; the interdependencies between human and non-human; the reverberations of history, above all post-colonial dimensions; the centrality of interdisciplinary knowledge and the very distinctive play of time across the issue. These six features provide the usually hidden conceptual scaffolding that structures all climate change stories. They also demonstrate why the goal of asserting a univocal consensus on climate science and politics fails to understand the past, present and likely futures of the topic. By turning down the volume and by inviting more voices to speak there is a good chance that more people will feel equipped and motivated to respond to this unusual problem.

What's the story?
Stories are the unit of currency for all media. Climate change has tended to be an ugly story for media producers and consumers — difficult both to tell and to hear. It is challenging to fit it into our most popular media forms, and has implications that most of us don't want to think or talk about. Given the conditions, most media globally have done a pretty good job of a 'bad' topic. They have been helped in this by the research and policy communities. Together those communities have offered most of the plot and characters in the first 25 years of mainstream media accounts of climate change. Most people surveyed

are aware of the notion of climate change and are concerned by it, and most of them reckon humans are at least partly responsible. The key conclusions of the IPCC's massive and diverse research review process have been widely communicated. These high levels of awareness and concern about climate change have come about above all because of media storytelling.

But climate change seems to run out of steam in politics and the media when it moves from 'worrying' to 'doing'. 'Business as usual' scenarios promise at best risky and at worst devastating outcomes. But the monotony of tone seems to quickly exhaust public interest.

Might this difficulty have something to do with some tactical moves taken in the past to mobilise public concern? A dominant framing of climate change — what I'll call 'the Gore narrative' — emerged in the early to mid 2000s. It promulgated the idea that 'the science is finished', a claim that rested on the promotion of an unassailable scientific consensus, as portrayed in *An Inconvenient Truth*. Martial and nationalist rhetoric, drawn from the second world war and the space race, set a tone for how society should respond to the science. But this tactic spoke to a very particular (American) political and cultural context, and even in that setting may have alienated as many people as it attracted.

In cultural terms, climate change is both more — and less — than a campaign anthem going by the title 'the greatest challenge facing humanity'. It is a difficult body of new knowledge that holds significance for every kind of challenge that humanity has always faced regarding shelter, comfort, food and mobility. In media terms, however, the topic often seems strangely disconnected from mainstream business, politics and home life. The time has come to invest in a wider range of accounts that embed this evolving field more fully in the everyday. One key task within this for the research and policy communities is to shift towards explaining climate change research as an immense process of risk assessment, and climate politics as one of humanity's most adventurous attempts at collective risk management. Such an apparently prosaic framing allows the science to be more open and interesting. It is a more accurate depiction of science practice and purpose. This move also helps the politics to connect more directly to a host of other more immediate concerns that people wake up to every day in terms of their own risk management about how they travel, how they look after their household and how they or their society protect against and spread physical or personal risks.

What *has* been communicated?

It is often said that the mainstream media are 'part of the problem' in terms of understanding and action on climate change. Certainly mainstream media performance has been uneven, with occasional epidemics of interest set within longer fallow periods where editors remain uninterested or sometimes hostile towards the topic. The main peaks of attention have come about in the early 1990s, culminating in the Earth Summit of 1992, and in the second half of the 2000s, marked by a combination of research and policy processes and media spectacles. The Copenhagen COP15 meeting of the UNFCCC in 2009 represented the most recent peak in attention. These peaks are part of a much longer pattern of waves and troughs of public and political attention to global environmental issues stretching back to the late 1950s.

It has been a consistent complaint of the environmental research and policy community since the first UN summit on environment in Stockholm in 1972 that the media repeatedly lose interest in their work despite its ongoing significance. But this fails to recognise that news and factual media storytelling demands conflict, event and personality. Climate change, with a few (often problematic) exceptions, offers the opposite. It seems almost designed to be ignored. The institutions developed to try to cope with the range and complexity of available knowledge on the topic, the IPCC and the UNFCCC, are science and policy institutions maintained by international civil servants and they link communities of researchers and policy specialists. Almost none of these people need to know what a media story is in order to do their job; indeed, it would probably make it more difficult if they did. Research and policy professionals require painstaking attention to well-logged detail, and careful testing of assumptions. Climate science and policy engages in slow and cautious deliberation and is required to practise anaemic 'good process'. The research and policy communities have generally invested little in communications. Specialist journalists have had to work against the tide of media culture to communicate the state of knowledge of climate science and policy. Global research into public attitudes suggests they have done a pretty good job in difficult conditions.

Opinion polling on these issues has been running for more than 30 years, albeit unevenly, around the world. Mirroring the paucity of media coverage of the topic in the developing world, and of consumer markets that support commercial opinion polling, results were much more scarce outside the developed world until well into the 2000s, but some data exist. The evidence points to quite widespread and steady awareness and concern, with peaks and troughs of public attention evident from the earliest polls. The troughs tend to coincide with economic downturns. A vast majority of the world's population is aware of climate change and a small majority understands it to be caused by humans. Since the early 1990s polling has shown that between 40 and 70% of people have been 'concerned' or 'very concerned'.

It is worth stopping to consider what an astonishing feat of communication this is. Climate change is difficult new knowledge. It demands innovation in the public imagination about the consequences of aggregates of individual acts. This is a grim extension of the green behaviour motto 'every little counts', and implies that everyone wrapped up in fossil fuel-based economies, that is, virtually everyone, holds some responsibility for this state of hazard. It introduces novel fears about how humans will live within an uncertain world. Despite these difficulties, most people around the world are aware of the issue and most of them are concerned about it.

Rather than berate the media for its failure to 'activate' a global public, we should acknowledge the fact that a story that defies the needs of media producers has been told at all. Despite its uncertainty, complexity and wearyingly slow pace the news has got out. This is not to suggest there is any need to stop telling it, but rather invites pause for thought: how should we tell this story *now*? It is a good time to ask the question, because the conditions of media production and consumption are changing fast, in ways that will have consequences for the next, long-postponed, phase: debating decisions about meaningful action.

Science = scandal = readers

In September 2013, a prominent comment piece by British columnist Christopher Booker in the *Daily Telegraph* newspaper was headlined, 'The ice is not melting, yet still the scaremongers blunder on'. After nearly a quarter of a century, the IPCC's scholarly, and for most of its history, obscure, review process, involving thousands of university researchers from numerous disciplines, finds itself tagged as 'blundering', 'alarmist', 'discredited' and a 'clique' in the pages of a prominent mainstream newspaper. Booker and friends seem wilfully ignorant of every aspect of contemporary research conditions, culture and practice. But there is no mystery behind that: it would get in the way of a sparky polemic — a good story.

Across the research community it is close to impossible to find anyone that does not think that humans are causing changes to the climate that are more likely than not to be hazardous — and potentially very dangerous. So why would an editor of a widely respected newspaper accept a steady flow of articles that are so at odds with the best available knowledge? For the answer you have to look to both the audience and at very recent changes in the media. This comment piece was flatly contradicted by factual reporting elsewhere in the paper in the same week. However the editor knows that the polemic serves to gather and comfort a significant portion of the paper's readership. Editorial perceptions of the attitudes and feelings of consumers are more influential than ever before: commissioning such opinion columns answers an appetite in an increasingly competitive market. Booker's column attracted more than 1,000 comments online — offering the editor another index of the relevance of his piece to the paper's readership.

The conditions of media decision-making and news consumption are now undergoing more rapid and far-reaching changes than at any time since the birth of broadcasting. These changes have erased some boundaries between media production and consumption. Phone providers are broadcasters; broadcasters produce acres of text; print media is consumed as much online as on paper, and their products integrate audio and video. These craft and technical changes are running in parallel with the steady concentration of media ownership into an ever-smaller number of increasingly international corporations. Digital media have seen parallel, often overlapping, processes of consolidation. Hence the attitudes of a shrinking number of proprietors and CEOs become more influential, with very mixed outcomes for climate change storytelling. Forceful and opinionated proprietors and editors can create atmospheres of permission or dismissal. From the CEO and/or proprietor through to the jobbing journalist, sub- and picture editor, everyone throughout that institution will be highly responsive to their customers/readers/users. (Everyone is struggling to find the right term: reader, viewer, or listener — none of these terms offer a full account any more. 'User' acknowledges extensions and overlaps that connect with social and other online media but is also problematic.)

The combination of new digital forms of direct feedback, and immediate intelligence about likes and dislikes, is re-shaping what it means to make an editorial decision within the media. Hence editors that serve conservative audiences in Australia, North America and the UK will be well aware that a significant proportion of their customers are alienated by news and other content about climate change. Climate contrarians (sometimes known as climate deniers or sceptics — both, for different reasons, inappropriate) ventriloquise the concerns of something between 20 and 40% of the population, and a greater percentage of politically right-leaning media consumers. Hence, while a few pages away the science or politics correspondents may offer clear factual content on climate change, the prejudices and worries of people alienated by 'the Gore narrative' will be read back to them, in the most robust terms.

'The people formerly known as the audience'

Running alongside changes in 'mainstream' media there have been some far-reaching developments in online and specifically social media. These developments blend production, consumption and sharing. There are more opportunities for unmediated knowledge exchange and debate between publics and professionals, including the emergence of prominent lay specialists. The opportunity for anyone with a screen and an internet connection to produce and share content is opening up the media spaces around environmental risks, spanning hyper-local to global concerns. Niche communities gather cheaply and quickly. Clay Shirky explains how most leisure time of the late twentieth century was given over to the unpaid part-time job of watching TV. He points to the extraordinary opportunities presented by the 'cognitive surplus' generated by educated populations with time available, and the cheap and powerful tools of digital media in their hands (Shirky, 2010).

The blogs and websites generated by climate change science and politics, and the communities of interest gathered around them, are prime examples of this process in action. The blogosphere has been a particularly significant media platform for climate contrarians. By the mid to late 2000s it had become comparatively rare to find news stories that sought to justify or sustain accounts contrary to the main thrust of climate science, although media cultures vary geographically and across time (see Painter, 2011; Boykoff and Nacu-Schmidt, 2013). However the blogosphere and other social media, particularly Twitter, offered an efficient means of identifying like minds and concentrating efforts. Although motivations for climate contrarianism do vary there are some generally very consistent themes. For most climate contrarians the issue represents an opportunity to exercise a set of concerns about the 'big state', taxation, intrusion into personal liberties, and fears of cosmopolitanism and shared international commitments.

There is a tendency in the climate change research and policy communities to dismiss contrarian blogs as 'astroturfing' (that is, produced by fake 'grassroots' organisations funded by fossil-fuel companies) but this fails to acknowledge the underlying ideological commitments of many of the people who give up very large portions of time to reading and writing about climate change. The emergence of lay specialists who don't publish in academic journals, but crowdsource critiques of climate science and policy, has helped to fill a hole for the mainstream media. For commercial media with substantial numbers of consumers who have been made anxious or irritated by the Gore narrative, the contrarian blogosphere provides a ready source of comments, quotes and background content. For public service media such as the BBC, giving some space to such parties or arguments offers a route to fulfilling expectations that they must serve all of their audiences, even if the assumptions of portions of the audience depart widely from the main body of published scientific knowledge. The inclusion of these voices frustrates the climate change research and policy community, while failing to stem charges of broadcasters' bias against contrarian positions.

The deployment of the Gore narrative through the mid 2000s led to an over-emphasis on certainties — an insistence that 'the science is finished' — a tactic designed to cope with the very narrow spaces of mainstream (old) media. This approach has been relentlessly punished in the more plural and discursive spaces of social media. Hence 'Climategate', a media storm generated around some ill-chosen phrases identified in several thousand private emails stolen from climate research institutions, became a focal point for contrarianism. The emails stretched back nearly a decade — long before the existence of social media. Several formal investigations exonerated the researchers who had been charged with dishonesty by contrarians, although these events pointed to the value and importance of more open processes around research data and public debate given the new media context. Although these stories appear ultimately to have had little impact on public opinion, they did influence the media mood, and nourished a sense that editors and journalists had been 'played' by an over-claiming climate lobby.

In these ways social media have helped to revive in the mainstream media a notion that had become largely discarded outside the US: that there exists a debate about whether climate change is happening or not, and if it is, whether it is primarily human-caused. This served to return conflict, event and personality to climate change as a media story, but also to distract media attention from the more pressing and properly contentious business of climate politics.

Once more with feeling?

Environmental research and policy communities continue to insist that the significance and urgency of these issues has not been absorbed by society. Faced with what they view as an uninterested media and passive publics there are continued cries of crisis, last chances and the promise of dire outcomes if warnings aren't heeded. This follows a long established pattern: it is more than four decades since one of the dominant media representations of environmental change was formed, that is: 'the end of the world as we know it is nigh — whenever nigh is'. These kinds of messages have helped to establish the notion of dire environmental hazard in the minds of many people, but it feels like a strategy with diminishing returns. It is a frame of reference that is dramatically at odds with some of the dominant trends in contemporary societies that are formed out of rapid social, technological and economic changes that have seen people shaping and presenting their own identities through increased consumption, communication, mobility and constant processes of reinvention. Hence while the climate change research and policy communities are casting around for a communications breakthrough that will overcome apparent indifference, strong trends in contemporary culture are flowing in the opposite direction. There are ways to work with these currents rather than against them. They include settling climate change within conversations about ambitions for a good personal and public quality of life, and about the risks that threaten them.

A game of risk

The latest phase of the global risk assessment was announced with the publication of the first part of IPCC AR5. It is now time for the research community to help the media towards a new reality, and social media can play a positive role. Today, post-Live Earth, post-COP15, post-Climategate, there is much to be gained by clearly stating that the research effort is a risk assessment rather than the burnishing and defence of a 'finished fact'. The research review process of the IPCC has been running for more than two decades and uncertainties have been narrowed in most areas of work, with others expanding in response to new findings. This opening up of new fields of uncertainty was anticipated in the very first IPCC report. This is science at work yet is often neglected in both campaigner and contrarian storytelling.

There is an opportunity now for the research community to inhabit and own the framing of their work as a process of risk assessment rather than allow it to be truncated and presented as an apparently static and finished 'consensus'. This would allow a portion of climate contrarians to feel more comfortable to engage with curiosity and openness with the research community's work, and vice versa. The remainder, who were never interested in the science but simply wanted to bang their ideological drum, would experience a much-diminished audience.

If climate science is seen as an ongoing global risk assessment then the policy work needs to be understood as risk management. By management I don't mean to suggest bureaucracy and managerialism but rather a rigorous approach to a well-defined problem, arrived at through the messy iterations of policy and politics. In most countries of the world this will be some form of democratically agreed process. The roles and responsibilities of risk assessor and manager are different. The Fire Brigade officer who assesses hazards in a block of flats doesn't get involved in ordering fire extinguishers and alarms but leaves this to the estate manager. The process is pretty similar when it comes to the assessment and management of global climate risks, albeit with a considerably wider range of people and skills involved. Once the best available information concerning a risk has been handed over, the manager has a duty to act on it. This is not to say that the path of action is going to be clear, but the responsibility to act certainly is. Neither does it suggest that there is a clear division between the two. There isn't. There are people and institutions who inhabit a fuzzy border zone, including some categories of researchers and some civil servants. So long as they and anyone looking at them know that they span the two then this can help make for better-targeted research and better-informed policy. The Risk Manager in Chief of any sovereign state that has accepted the IPCC's risk assessment is the President or Prime Minister. Their performance in response to the climate change risk assessment will increasingly be considered one of the key indicators of their general performance. Politics and the media need to actively interrogate what commitments to stabilise and reduce emissions, and preparations to cope with unpredictable climate changes, really mean. There is no shortage of stories here: changed prices for commodities; sunrise for some new technologies and trades; sunsets for others and major interventions in transport, planning and agriculture. But will a focus on climate politics rather than another round of the truth wars about climate science increase the topic's media presence and in turn reinforce its political relevance?

One promising route to a more vibrant public conversation about climate change actions is to frame them as a question of collective insurance against collective risks. This insurance takes the form of reducing the chances of harm and increasing our chances of coping with events should they come to pass. An insurance frame is one that is familiar to industry, policy and households, and collective insurance takes varied forms. Car drivers find laws requiring insurance intuitive and fair. In countries with universal welfare provisions unexpected needs are met through collective risk sharing and paid for through a steady drip-feed of financial contributions. A collective risk management and societal insurance framework helps pave the way for a redrafting of the costs of carbon. This can include an assessment of the social and environmental costs now and in the future. This invites a crisp public debate about how and at what level to tax the 'bads' of pollution and reward and support 'goods' like wage income and investment. And the precise division of something like a carbon charge dividend would make for energetic debates. Should funds be used to protect those vulnerable to climate change impacts, to invest in large scale technology and infrastructure investments, to offer tax breaks to green entrepreneurs, or some combination of these? The libertarians of left and right who fear the 'meddling of climate change nannies' would likely be a far more incisive and positive presence in a debate about such choices than they are in their often ill-considered and manipulative commentaries on the science.

Policies and actions that help societies to mitigate and to be better prepared to cope with climate change impacts are stories about cities, houses, streets, food, travel and the stuff we use. In their role as risk managers, politicians must become assertive about their own ideas for cutting greenhouse gas emissions in ways that deliver an improved quality of life and greater collective security. This would be made easier if environmental NGOs recovered their gift for cultural entrepreneurship. Rather than trying to generate popular concern at prospective climate chaos they need to open up public debates about the quality and nature of everyday life at work, in the street and at home. Reductions in CO_2 emissions can and should lead to the creation of more healthy, comfortable and convivial lives and a more robust economy. Preparing societies to cope with the impacts of climate change, including floods, droughts and storms, may also serve to equip them to cope better with a range of other challenges. But no one institution or political party holds that route map. We are likely to find our way by looking a few feet ahead of us into the dark, and the media can hold the torch.

A new place in the world

Framing the scientific research effort around climate change as a risk assessment will serve to return it to the relative obscurity of most academic work. This will open the way to telling a different set of stories about why it matters. The immense interdisciplinary effort around climate change is, amongst other things, one of the most ambitious shared questions we have in front of us. We are encountering difficult new knowledge, and don't always agree about how to respond. This way of thinking is very different to universalising proclamations regarding 'the greatest challenge facing humanity'. Amongst other things this shift of emphasis allows climate change research to become interesting, even enchanting. Explaining it as a backroom risk assessment operation, and inviting everyone into that back room to understand it better and talk about how it is being conducted, will help to build trust and engagement. Those changes in media practice and culture that have seen social and mainstream media become intertwined can be put to work to open up access to the daily practices of climate change research in all its mad diversity. This can and should include every corner of that work, and not confine itself, as the media has tended to, to the natural sciences. Climate change has been a strong driver of innovation in engineering and design, and is spurring fresh thinking in the arts, humanities and social sciences also. It is generating new thinking on lighting, mobility, communications, architecture, food and energy, and in so doing generating stories that would be compelling to many of the people alienated by the currently dominant chorus of projected woe.

Allowing the topic its full cultural scope may also serve to open up the public imagination in ways that can make the politics of climate change more dynamic. The difficult new knowledge about climate change propels us into new ways of thinking about humanity's place in the world. Just as with policy, responses will vary widely, and will be informed by people's existing values and commitments. But one idea will not survive in this new intellectual and ethical climate. It will no longer be possible to think of humans as wholly dominant in a benign seedbed prepared for the sole purpose of their flourishing. Increased sensitivity to the interdependence between social, economic and ecological systems will help to take most people to a more accurate notion of humanity's rather modest place in the world. And our notion of that world won't be of a fragile thing, or a tool in the hand, but rather a dynamic system that we inhabit and help to make, and that we need to respect and love for its complex and changeable nature.

Greenland: How the National Theatre created a climate change play

Kellie C. Payne

The story of *Greenland* begins with Nicholas Hytner, Director of the National Theatre in London. One of his main ambitions has been that the National should respond to current affairs. 'It's a great time to be a national theatre, and to rise to the challenge of living up to our name,' he wrote. 'We want to tell the stories that chart the way the nation is changing. We want to bring front-line reports from new communities and generations, and we want to see the present redefined in the context of the past.'[1] After the Copenhagen Summit, in December 2009, climate change became one of those stories.

The original idea for *Greenland* was that it should be similar to *The Power of Yes: A Dramatist Seeks to Understand the Financial Crisis*, David Hare's 2009 play analysing the causes of the 2008 financial crash. In an interview for this essay, *Greenland*'s dramaturg Ben Power said that Hytner 'talked about how important he thought it was that the National Theatre was engaging with hot issues and was finding new ways to help its audience engage with issues, which felt relevant and important and things which were in the news and which normally were not the subject matter for theatre in this building'. Hytner wanted the new play to have a similar approach to *The Power of Yes*. 'Nick was keen that we found a way of doing something on the subject of climate change and the environment that had the same kind of research base and the same kind of journalistic objectivity in the way it was put together'.

The first discussions between Hytner, Power, and the play's director, Bijan Sheibani, took place in late spring 2010. The play was to open in February 2011. As Sheibani says, 'It was quite a quick thing to put together'. They started with just the subject. 'We didn't have a play, we didn't have writers, anything, apart from Nick saying to me and Ben, "We want to do a play about climate change. Bijan, you'll be the director; Ben, you're going to bring it all together, do the dramaturgy"'.

This was very different to how the National usually approached issue-based works. 'What might have happened in the past,' Power says, 'was a single writer would be commissioned to go off and write a play'.

'*The Power of Yes* was a play about the economy,' says Sheibani. 'It basically asked the question, "what happened to make the world economy crash?" I guess the question around climate change is less clear'.

'We thought that one of the big differences between the financial crash and the environment,' says Power, 'was just the breadth of the issue, the complexity of the issue, and our own confusion and uncertainty surrounding it. We wanted to find a way of reflecting that, and that's what led to the commissioning of four writers to find different ways into the subject'.

The subject matter itself influenced the form the piece would take. 'We felt very immediately — everybody, including Nick and the literary department — that the form of it should be multi-voiced.' The team felt that complexity was inherent in the topic. 'It became clear very quickly in the process,' says Power, 'that the main theme was the unknowable — chaos. What do you do about the fact that there are things that you don't have answers [to]? That needed something that was more partial and was about subjectivity. That was the biggest challenge of the piece'.

One of the first decisions, then, was to commission four writers. Usually, says Power, 'you get this enormous authority given to the playwright. For example with *The Power of Yes*, it was an instance of "I, David Hare, will understand what's going on and I will come back and tell you".' Power didn't feel that was appropriate for this issue. 'Every person you ask tells you something different. So we thought that an honest way to represent that might be to have a number of writers. And indeed, each [writer started] in a very different place, and had a different set of instincts about the issue, and their research went in different directions'.

Sheibani and Power split the writing burden between four playwrights: Moira Buffini, Matt Charman, Penelope Skinner and Jack Thorne. It allowed them to research the topic as a group, but to have four different approaches to the subject. 'We thought long and hard about who we should approach,' says Sheibani, 'and we've got four writers who all have very different qualities to their writing but who we thought would be able to respond to the material as well' (Platform discussion).

Most science plays, Kirsten Shepherd-Barr explains in her study *Science on Stage*, are written by well-established authors who are known for their dramas on other topics. 'They are first experienced dramatists and second interested in exploring science' (Shepherd-Barr, 2006: 47). They often chose to write about science because they have a general interest in broader philosophical and epistemological concepts which they may have already explored in other plays. Similarly, *Greenland*'s authors were dramatists first, with a secondary interest in climate change.

One factor in the decision to have four writers was the time constraint. They would have just six months to research and write a play which would go into rehearsals in November 2011. For Power, having four writers was central to the overall concept. 'We would create something which we felt reflected the vast variety of tone and type of thing one needs to talk about: politics and science and issues of personal choice. That, it seems to me, necessitates a variety of styles and idioms that's reflected in the final piece and the production' (Platform discussion).

Once the four writers were chosen, the research began. According to the National, the team 'spent six months interviewing key individuals from the worlds of science, politics, business and philosophy in an effort to understand our changing planet.' In the programme for *Greenland*, a list appears of 41 experts who were consulted: journalists, scientists, government representatives, cultural representatives, academics, campaigners, an economist, two climate sceptics, and the chairman of Shell.

One of those consulted was Charlie Kronick, Senior Climate Change Advisor at Greenpeace. In an interview for this essay, he recalled spending a couple of hours with the four writers, the director, the stage design team and the dramaturg. They asked him questions about nuclear power and the science of climate change. But, in Kronick's mind, the questions 'bore no resemblance or had any bearing on the final play as far as I could tell'. He remembers them asking questions such as 'What are the complexities of the science?' and found them to be 'interested in the civil society response, so that's why they asked about nuclear power'. Kronick made a recommendation: 'I said to them, the last thing you want to do is have a play about whether or not it's happening or what the scientific controversies are'. He went further. 'I just said I didn't think that was fundamentally the interesting bit. It's about the politics. I spent quite a lot of time talking about the north/south relationships, about power relationships, about how it related to broader issues of economy and trade. I tried to contextualise it'.

Kronick found the production team to be relatively unaware of the main physical and political aspects of climate change. 'They seemed to have no contact with any of what I would have thought were the key aspects.' This includes the politics of climate change and climate change activism. 'They didn't know what were the fundamental physical questions being asked and they didn't really understand the politics at all'. However, as he adds, 'the politics are really complicated. It's not really surprising'.

Both Sheibani and playwright Matt Charman admit that most of the team didn't know much about climate change. 'I have to confess,' Sheibani says, 'I don't feel qualified to talk about the subject. The more I looked into it, the more daunted I was by the subject and by the scale of it, by the number of factors involved, economically, scientifically, socially. It's incredibly difficult to articulate'. Charman describes their first meeting. 'We worked out after about 40 minutes that none of us really knew anything about climate change'. However, for Charman, this was a good starting place. He thought this was 'very liberating because I think once you start to realise this topic is so vast and you know so little about it you start to think: what are the big questions that we've got'. Ignorance brought its own advantages. 'You actually start to assume the position of your audience, walking in off the street'. Furthermore, he says, 'I think you start to assume that mindset and you break it down and you say, OK, so what are the areas of the subject that we really are fascinated by, confused by, and then you start to talk about those things' (Platform discussion). Moira Buffini explained that at the beginning of the process, the writers started out with a long list of questions: 'We wrote pages of questions... just loads and loads of questions' (Platform discussion).

What were the questions? Sheibani outlined the separate lines that they followed:

The strands to this enquiry are scientific, political, but also they make me think a lot about our own lives and how we think and [...] our own dreams and our own relationships, so it's a very small subject in many ways. How one relates to your own house, your own family, but as well it's a huge political and scientific subject. There's lots of maths and science in it as well. So we knew we were going to have to convey data and convey relationships between people. So, in terms of form, we were looking for a way of doing that. It became clear that video would be very useful in terms of science and geography and statistics. But we also needed something poetic as well because the subject matter does demand poetry because it is about a very old subject, an apocalypse, which I think we've looked at for centuries. (Platform discussion)

They read too. 'We read a lot of books.... things like *Heat* [George Monbiot] or books with storms in the title or grandchildren.' (Sheibani is presumably referring to *Storms of my Grandchildren: The Truth About the Coming Climate Catastrophe and Our Last Chance to Save Humanity* by climate scientist James Hansen.) Power further explains, 'We were doing a lot of work with the writers and a group of actors, lots of improvisation, trying things out, reading bits of documentary material and interviewing people'.

Trips were made to the Met Office Hadley Centre, a climate change research centre in Exeter, and to the Houses of Parliament, to watch a subcommittee interviewing experts on climate change. They also spoke to people who had been to the Copenhagen Summit. 'We met a lot of people,' says Sheibani. 'Just collected information. And then it was really up to the writers to absorb that information and... It depends on the writer, they have very different ways of using that information. Someone like Jack will absorb it, he'll just write what's in his heart'.

After the research, the writers wrote their own storylines. Sheibani explained that the individual storylines could be broken down as follows: Jack Thorne created Harry and Harold, the two aspects of a scientist who observes black guillemots in Alaska. Moira Buffini wrote about Lisa, who leaves her postgraduate teaching course to become a full-time climate campaigner. Matt Charman wrote about policy advisor Phoebe and scientist Ray. Penelope Skinner wrote dialogue for a lesbian couple as well as parodic 'Deal or No Deal' monologues with a character called Adeel. Some sections of the play were improvised with the company. For example, scenes set at the Copenhagen Summit were devised by the company from interviews with the UN representative Joanna Depledge.

Buffini spoke about how difficult it was to know how to pitch their writing.

> You're writing a play for an audience, some of whom will be experts, and some of whom will know nothing, and so all you can do I think as a writer is write from your heart, and try and touch on how this subject has affected you. I think that's what we all did.

This became problematic. 'You don't have a clear loud single authorial voice going, "I think this...", but I think it reflects the subject more honestly in that you have various voices going, "this is almost bigger than we can fit in our heads"' (Platform discussion).

How could four separate writing strands be brought together into one coherent play? 'They wrote completely independently from each other,' says Sheibani. 'That was difficult. We essentially had four different plays, four different voices' (Platform discussion).

One of the aspects of new writing that drama critic Aleks Sierz highlights is the strength of a singular voice. There is a widely held expectation among critics and audiences that 'new writing' represents an expression of what playwright Tim Fountain has characterised as a 'singular original voice' with a 'very particular vision'. Or as playwright Phyllis Nagy puts it: 'Plays are *written*. They are usually written by a single person in possession of an idiosyncratic style and... a single, intelligent, evocative point of view' (quoted in Sierz, 2011: 49). It would later strike a number of critics that these were the qualities that *Greenland* lacked. A common criticism of the play was the confusion caused by having a multi-authored script.

Sheibani says that each playwright had written a more or less coherent piece which was then divided into separate scenes and spliced together to form a single piece of theatre. Power says that they didn't want to impose an arbitrary structure on the play. 'You want to try to find a structure which serves where the ideas are going, the way the writing is evolving. But there are rehearsals and there are actors who need to learn parts and it's a very delicate and quite organic thing' (Platform discussion).

Ben Power found that 'there were connections between the plays and the plays ended up sharing a structure without having one imposed on them'. He was excited by 'the way the various narrative strands came together and the shape does feel coherent and like it had some kind of plan behind it, even though it didn't' (Platform discussion).

However, for Sheibani, one part of the play that he might have changed, had they had more time, was its structure. He says that he 'might have gotten involved in one story before exploding out into all the stories'. For instance, to have begun 'with the scientist and politician, followed that through and then exploded out of that into all the other things'. As it is, 'it's quite choppy at the beginning, so you don't know which story to hold onto, you don't know what the main story is. You don't know who to care about'. Yet Power believes that this disjuncture in the narrative, and the multi-voice nature of the play, 'was enormously powerful and... broke some of the rules of the way in which we think conventional dramatic action has to happen. Things were cut against each other and it was choppy and a bit dislocated and a bit broken but that felt authentic, that's what it feels like when you start to look at the issue'.

Some of the topics that were considered very important proved almost impossible to dramatise. 'There was lots of improvisation around the Stern Review,' says Buffini, 'and "cap and trade", which is another economic means of trying to control climate change, and it was so difficult to explain.' Power remembers that 'Jack became obsessed with the Stern Review but couldn't in the end find the right dramatic form'. Charman adds, 'Crucially, as well, we realised that it wasn't at the heart of the subject' (Platform discussion). 'The thing that became clear,' says Power, 'was there was going to be no way we could give any definitive response or official response. All it could ever be was the bits that we were interested in, that we could find theatrical form for'. A number of themes were considered, but in the end rejected. 'A huge amount of energy and time was spent thinking about solutions,' says Power, 'about technologies, carbon capture, alternative energy, and quite advanced engineering solutions, long-term engineering solutions, and that was all fascinating, but impossible really to find a dramatic way of doing it unless you were to write a play set in the lab'.

During the Platform discussion with actors and members of the *Greenland* creative team, Buffini was asked whether the writers had considered the sceptics' arguments. 'It's not a 50/50 argument, it's like a 95/5 per cent argument really', she replied. It was, in fact, Buffini who wrote the one sceptical voice in the play. Al, the father of activist Lisa, quotes climate sceptic Nigel Lawson in discussions with his daughter, and questions the veracity of anthropogenic climate change. Sceptical voices were included in the wider programme of events accompanying the production: Nigel Lawson presented a Platform event entitled 'An Appeal to Reason: A Cool Look at Global Warming' on 4 April 2011. No one chaired the event. Lawson explained that he 'was originally invited here to do a debate but nobody would debate me'. He questioned the predicted sea level rises and stated that climate change mitigation threatened to cripple the economy.

One of the most praised elements of the play was the show's theatricality and staging. 'This is the first play that I've worked on,' says Charman, 'that really needed to come to the stage'. The performance space was the National's proscenium stage, the Lyttelton. For Sheibani, scenes set in the Arctic, using elements such as snow and wind, were integral to the play's imagery. 'We'd be drawn to certain parts of the subject because we were thinking: what would that be like on stage? What would the design for that be?' Company members were interested in 'all sorts of visual metaphors'. For instance, at the end of the play, sheets of paper fell from the sky. Another visual motif that was prevalent was the use of plastic and rubbish that accumulated on the stage. 'The plastic island in the Pacific Ocean really drew us all in,' says Sheibani.

Reviewers noted the array of technological effects. Critic Aleks Sierz describes these as ranging from

> direct address to vivid projections, from flashing strobes to huge percussive effects, and from multiple-choice questions to rain storms made of paper. And there's a real rain storm too. And flashing birds flying around the auditorium, and airborne supermarket trolleys. Pop songs — 'It's Raining Men!' — make the heart beat faster. (Sierz, 2011a)

For Sierz 'the piece's most wonderful surprise' was an animatronic polar bear. It also appealed to most of the other reviewers. In *The Times*, Libby Purves wrote: 'It doesn't stay long, but after the first interminable hour its advent is such a relief that we applaud.' The theatricality of the production was attributed to Sheibani's direction and Bunny Christie's stage design. In *The Guardian*, Michael Billington wrote that Christie had created 'a world on the verge of disintegration.'

The National Theatre's marketing strategy relied heavily on the large number of scheduled events which coincided with the production. These included the Talkaoke, presented by participatory artists 'The People Speak'. Installed in the lobby of the theatre, the Talkaoke featured a moderator with a microphone who invited members of the audience to discuss any issues arising from the play. After a matinee show, a group of Dutch schoolchildren took part. One boy said, 'I don't think it's the small things, it needs to be the world leaders, they need to come up with clear ideas'. Another replied, 'I don't think this is very realistic. If we have seven billion people who can do small things it will accumulate. The seven billion can do more than the one hundred.' One of the girls said, 'The main thing that I got from this play and this issue is that it can't be just individuals and it can't be just big corporations or the government, it has to be everyone doing anything they can. It has to be people working together'.

There was also an extensive series of 'Platform' discussions. Guest speakers included Charlie Kronick of Greenpeace, Bjørn Lomborg, who presented a talk entitled 'Cool It!: The Sceptical Environmentalist's Guide to Global Warming', John Shepherd, Earth system scientist, who presented 'Earth System Modelling', and Tim Flannery, palaeontologist and environmentalist (author of *Here on Earth: A New Beginning*). Biologist George Divoky, the inspiration for the character of Harry, the observer of Alaskan guillemots, discussed the role with Michael Gould, the actor who played him.

As Kristen Shepherd-Barr explains, there is a tradition of creating public awareness of science attached to the production of science plays. This may take the form of performance-linked symposia, with experts in science, history and theatre providing information to complement the production. Michael Frayn's *Copenhagen*, for instance, had a symposium and a pre- or post-performance audience 'talk back'. This is not a new phenomenon — there are precedents in theatre history. In nineteenth-century France, experts explained plays to audiences in pre-performance lectures. The critic Michael Billington thought that discussions about climate change might be better tackled in this forum than in the play itself. 'I have a hunch, in fact, that the plethora of pre-show platforms will generate as much drama as we find in a play that stabs the conscience without offering a perceptible point of view.'

Within the National Theatre's marketing plan, there was an analysis of *Greenland* that drew out possible strengths, weaknesses, threats and opportunities. Among the strengths identified was the play's theme, the environment, and the idea of new writers participating in a unique collaborative process. However, the marketing team felt that *Greenland* 'could be perceived as "not for me" if positioned as a "lecture" play'. (Other threats included opening after the Christmas break and the play coinciding with two other plays, the star-studded *Frankenstein* and Alan Ayckbourn's *Season's Greetings*.) The opportunities highlighted by the team included the chance to build suspense around what was deemed an 'exciting new theatrical process' and it was suggested that the creative journey of the play be highlighted. Further, emphasis was placed on the 'strong opportunity for online debate and discussion', the platform events and the educational possibilities to create resources and encourage school groups to participate.

During the Platform discussion, an audience member asked the panel the following question:

I'm still trying to figure out the fundamental purpose of this venture from the point of view of the audience. To try and change our understanding, sort of a missionary purpose, to try and make us more aware, or enrich our understanding of the issue, or is it fundamentally an artistic purpose that this happens to be the subject but it's an opportunity to get the audience to have an artistic experience. What really is it for? Because it seemed from your presentation that the desire to do something connected with climate change came before the development or the actual purpose.

Ben Power, one of the panellists, replied:

I think the starting point of this play was let's have a public conversation about this subject. Nobody at any point said, 'Let's make a play that makes people want to do this...' or act in that way. It was very much, 'Let's start a conversation', and I think that I should also say that the idea of experiments in theatre, or experiments in art, gets thrown around quite a lot. This was genuinely an experiment in this building, to commission something, to programme it before there is anything on paper. I think it is a commitment that this building has and this institution has for starting public conversations. The fact that it didn't have a predetermined end before the start is what makes this a really unusual place.

The discussion's moderator that evening was Sebastian Born, the literary manager at the National:

The starting place for any conversation is to make a good piece of theatre, which is artistically successful and viable, imaginative and engages the audience in theatre and metaphor, and all of the things that we know that theatre can do when it's successful.

Another questioner asked the playwrights what they thought they were doing when they wrote the play. Buffini replied, 'I think it's hubristic for any artist to try to change somebody's mind'. Power added: 'This is an unusual project in that it was initiated as an attempt to be part of the most important conversation that's going on currently'. Charman summed up his perspective on their objectives:

There was a unique challenge with this one because as we went on this journey, we learned stuff, facts, statistics, and we thought we do need to communicate this, as well as a great piece of art, but I think where it got really interesting for us, and where I think all pieces of theatre get interesting, is when there are questions without answers presented to the audience. We're not here to tell you what to think, but we're here presenting you with where we got to on our journey and to share the questions that are perplexing us.

Buffini added: 'It seems to me that the big question of the play is, "What do we do?" It's about people who are all trying to do something about this great crisis.'

Sheibani wanted the audience 'to be thinking about the subject more'. The play was intended to 'inform them a bit. Convey some facts about it, but show them how our processes, ways of dealing with it, aren't working at the moment. More just look at what's happened so far with the way people have tried to solve it.' He made a general point. 'Theatre's always stronger if you're not teaching, you're not being didactic. To criticise the play, I think it veered on that, it's hard not to with this subject, to try not to teach people. We'd learnt so much stuff, we really wanted to convey it to people.'

Kirsten Shepherd-Barr observes that there tends to be a divide in science plays between those which are didactic and attempting to educate the audience and those who use science in an 'aesthetically integrated way'. As she puts it, 'There are many science plays whose scientific content is unassailable but whose theatricality is weak. They may teach science, but they do not make superb or even satisfying drama' (Shepherd-Barr, 2006:12).

Greenland opened early in February 2011 and the reviews were mixed. The average rating according to the website *whatsonstage.com* was two stars, and the newspapers ranged between two-star reviews (*Evening Standard*, *Daily Mail* and *The Times*) and three stars (the *Guardian* and *The Independent*). Aleks Sierz's review for *theartsdesk.com* was characteristic:

A large ensemble cast, and some fine individual performances, means that *Greenland* is two hours of engrossing, sometimes funny, occasionally frustrating, often striking, but never really overwhelming debate that at worst feels like a lecture, and at best a soothing balm for liberal audience members who'd like to be challenged, but just not very much. (Sierz, 2011a)

Michael Coveney in *whatsonstage.com* also conveyed the divided nature of the play's reception, saying 'Greenland is... skilful, enjoyable in odd moments and strikingly staged... But it's dead at the centre and therefore dead in the water'. At least four reviewers, Paul Taylor in *The Independent*, Aleks Sierz (again) for *The Stage*, Sarah Hemming in the *Financial Times* and Michael Billington in the *Guardian* all positively acknowledge the attempts the play made to tackle the topic of climate change. For instance, Taylor notes, 'the evening is undeniably stimulating. It brings home vividly how the debate is not on a level playing field and comes stuffed with historical baggage'. Sierz says, 'this is a play that takes climate change seriously, but with a human perspective... there are regular brief showers of humour to moisten the potential aridity of the subject matter'. Billington notes that 'at least one thing is clear: climate change is a divisive topic. You could argue that the play accurately reflects society's fractured uncertainty over how to tackle climate change: through political negotiation, disruptive demonstrations or myriad individual gestures'.

Two reviewers refer to the play as 'kaleidoscopic'. Billington wrote of its 'kaleidoscope of intersecting narratives' which he claims results in a production that 'while well staged, lacks focus'. Hemming uses the same adjective: 'a downside of this kaleidoscopic approach is that nothing beds in and there is little real progress'. Billington goes on to say, 'what we get is a somewhat confusing multi-perspective mosaic.' Critics questioned the extent to which the play offered new information, or whether it was likely to shift opinion. According to Sierz, 'while the play offers plenty of variety, most of what it tells us we already know'. For Billington, the 'show is unlikely to shift anyone's perspective'. Some reviewers, Charles Spencer of the *Daily Telegraph* in particular, felt no ambivalence. 'The NT is now offering two punishing hours of strident polemic on the subject that generates enough heat to melt a polar ice cap but doesn't provide a single ray of illuminating light'. He concluded that the play was 'one of the shrillest and most irritating shows in recent memory'.

A good deal of the criticism centred on the characters. Paul Taylor praised the production as 'not so much a play as an intellectual extravaganza' and a 'clever, topical, many-stranded piece'. However, he found 'something in me that resists' the play. I care about the issues. But I couldn't give a damn about any of the multiply-authored characters'. Sarah Hemming agreed. 'The characters are thinly drawn, their relationships flimsy and their arguments often grimly clichéd. Theatre can be excellent at dialectic, or at plunging you into characters' lives. This piece doesn't do either: it neither rattles your brain cells nor stirs your emotions'.

Greenpeace's Charlie Kronick had deep reservations about the way in which activism was portrayed in the play.

They were all caricatures. What's interesting about climate change is that most of the people involved in it aren't, funnily enough. It's a pretty rich cast of characters and it's a fantastic kind of proxy for the big issues around the tensions between the emerging economies and the established economies, old politics and new politics, youth and age, north and south. There's so many things you could've explored. And they didn't explore any of them. And they just stuck with those types and easily identified tropes.

Michael Billington attributes the poor character development to the playwrights' methodology. 'The show starts with a big issue and then seeks ways to illustrate it. I suspect it would be more fruitful to take the more traditional route of beginning with characters and a situation and working outwards.'

The director and the dramaturg defended *Greenland*. Sheibani commented that it's 'almost impossible to make a piece about the subject because you're really talking about the way the whole world is structured, aren't you?' He felt that it was perhaps because of this that the play received negative criticism.

I think people were expecting to come and see the National Theatre's take on the subject of climate change, and I think there's a bit of a backlash from the broadsheets because you know we weren't giving them something tangible, something satisfying to hold onto. It was a bit messy. We felt we were being true to the messiness of the subject.

Power echoed Sheibani's feelings about why the play wasn't well received: 'It was expected that it would be polished and have a clear position and express it in quite a conventional way. And it didn't do any of those things'. For Power there is a 'disjuncture' between what the audience expected from a play about climate change from the National Theatre and what *Greenland* managed to achieve:

When the National Theatre does anything, it appears to be the establishment making a statement about something. We are the establishment, in cultural terms, even if not in political terms, but certainly in the theatre community, this is as official as it gets and we wanted to make something which was a bit strange and not certain of what it was and a bit uneasy and uneven and it's very hard to reconcile that with — 'Here is the National Theatre's statement about climate change'. Its statement about climate change is that it doesn't really know what it thinks about climate change and that was a disjuncture which was hard.

Despite a mixed reception, *Greenland* represents an inventive attempt by the National Theatre to cope with an unusually demanding topic. The National hired four playwrights to address the topic from a range of perspectives, yet its director, dramaturg and writers all struggled to convey the breadth and complexities of climate-change within one piece. The work was met with mixed reviews, some commending its visuality and boldness while others struggled with what they found to be its didactic tone and unevenly drawn characters. As a well resourced, albeit hurried, experiment in climate change theatre the production demonstrates the many and varied challenges of dramatising the topic.

1   www.nationaltheatre.org.uk/7083/history-of-the-nt/history-of-the-national.html. Thanks to those who agreed to be interviewed for the purposes of this research: Bijan Sheibani (10 July 2012), Ben Power (5 September 2012) and Charlie Kronick (29 March 2012). Further quotations from these contributors and the four playwrights are taken from the Platform discussion about *Greenland* on 3 February 2011 at the National Theatre (cited as 'Platform discussion'). References for reviews of *Greenland* quoted here can be found in the Bibliography.

What shall we tell the children?

Alice Bell

The connection between children, media and that occasionally green-tinged thing we might call the environment runs deep. There are also ways in which children inspire concern about the future — whilst simultaneously invoking nostalgia — which can lead to environmental campaigns either featuring images of childhood or appealing to young audiences directly.

The various symbols, ideologies and objects caught up at the intersection of children and the environment have changed over time. Cultural concepts of both nature and the child have changed significantly over the last few centuries, as have the politics of environmental change.

This essay considers some recent green-themed media aimed at young people. It takes a close look at the character of the eco superhero, but also considers the materiality of such media, and pays particular attention to notions of agency (in other words: who is being asked to act; what are they being encouraged to do?). I take the question of 'what shall we tell the children?' as a lead here. I don't pretend to offer any concrete answers, but rather reflect and question some of the assumptions made.

Writing children, books and nature

Hidden in Jacqueline Rose's widely read 1994 study of *Peter Pan* is a short critique of Alan Garner's *The Stone Book Quartet*. Here she argues that Garner, like many other children's authors before him, uses the child as a symbol for something before socialisation — before science even — in contrast to the apparent reduction, degradation and alienation of modernity. An untouched landscape is seen as the truer, realer and safer one, with the Romantic view of the child employed as its icon. There's a long history of Romanticism in children's literature. Romanticisms vary, in their aims and interpretation, but it is a reasonably common trope to see a child as imbued with a special connection to Nature. As Rose neatly puts it:

> Garner, like Rousseau two centuries before him, places on the child's shoulders the responsibility for saving humankind from the degeneracy of modern society [...] the child is constantly set up as the site of a lost truth. (Rose, 1994: 43)

You can insert your own theoretical scare quotes around 'nature' in all of this, and pick your favourite philosopher/ sociologist to do so. The key point to take from Rose is that many children's books apply a rather limited view of what nature might be, which in turn might connect to a similarly narrow view of what children might be.

Similar arguments to Rose's analysis of Garner have been raised elsewhere in children's literature scholarship. Perry Nodleman (1985), for example, offers an interesting analysis of science fiction aimed at young adults. Noting several books which feature a child character travelling away from modernist, *Metropolis*-like urban environments and towards apparently older, agriculturally based societies which are ultimately discovered to be more fulfilling, he suggests that a narrative of growth in the child is used to critique a modernist view of technological and social progress. Noga Applebaum (2006) goes further, and argues in the context of more recent titles that there is a tendency to criticise technology in children's books. I'm not sure I agree it is a straightforward anti-science and technology attitude. As the twenty-first century vogue for young adult steampunk shows, even when children's books represent technology, they can be rather nostalgic in stance with ambivalent attitudes (Bell, 2009). Farah Mendelsohn (2007) makes the pertinent point that child characters tend to be constructed as relatively passive in respect to science and technology, not the builders of their futures so much as 'future users in waiting'.

We can see differently structured, but nonetheless similar, conceptualisations played out in non-fiction too. Nature study guides for young people sometimes assume children will have an inherent love of the natural world. As Aileen Fyfe (2003) argues, nature was a favourite topic for publishers such as the Religious Tract Society and the Society for Promoting Christian Knowledge because children were assumed to be 'naturally' curious about nature, and examination of the natural world was assumed to lead easily to contemplation of the Creator. These books presented nature as God's creation, something worth describing so it could be marvelled at. As children's non-fiction and various cultures of science changed throughout the twentieth century, the religious element went from non-fiction books for general audiences, but it is perhaps interesting that nature books are still generally sold separately from science ones.

Greening children's media
More modern green ideas started to make their way into children's books — fiction and other — in the 1970s just as they appeared in other parts of popular culture. They were joined by new media as they emerged (children's television, computer games, and so on). These new introductions happened in the context of shifting media cultures and changing ideas of childhood and (youth) political agency. Michael Foreman's *Dinosaurs And All that Rubbish* (1972) and Dr Seuss's *The Lorax* (1971) make nice case studies from the 1970s, if only because they remain so popular. For slightly older readers you can also see environmental issues within post-apocalyptic literature from the 1970s onwards (e.g. Mary Wesley's *The Sixth Seal*, 1969).

There was a small boom in environmental non-fiction in the early 1990s surrounding the Rio Earth Summit in 1992. For example, the long-running British television show Blue Peter established a 'green' badge (a rare new edition of its prized Blue Peter badges) to compete for. Mirroring wider media peaks and troughs of attention, there was another boom in the mid-2000s, part of the wave of activity which dropped off after the Copenhagen UN COP15 in 2009. Analysis of late twentieth-century green youth media reflected a sense that environmental issues were seen as kids' topics because it was assumed children had some connection to nature, but also that the new environmental politics was future-facing. The idea of jeopardy in 'save the planet' messaging was seen as especially relevant to young audiences. Some have suggested that framing ecology as a children's issue offers a way of devolving responsibility to younger generations (Buckingham, 2000: 45). Others have observed that young people act/are encouraged to act as environmentalist activists within their families via a green-tinged form of 'pester power' (Odell, 2009).

Arguably, children's media tend towards optimism, even if the symbolic use of child characters in literature aimed at adults can be applied to quite dystopic ends, as in for example, Cormac McCarthy's *The Road* or P.D. James' *Children of Men* (in both the novels and film adaptations). Or, take the use of child protagonists in the UK Department for Energy and Climate Change's *Bedtime Stories* campaign in 2009, which led to over 900 complaints to the Advertising Standards Agency. Based on some research suggesting parents would be more likely to act on climate change if they thought their children were at risk, one advert depicted a man reading to his daughter. The narration starts: 'There was once a land where the weather was very, very strange', then cuts to an animation of the pages showing a bunny rabbit character crying, before moving back to the face of the child who looks increasingly concerned. The narration continues with references to scientists warning of carbon emissions and an illustration of CO_2 as an angry monster in the sky, with puppies drowning underneath. It ends with the narrator suggesting that maybe if the adults cut CO_2 they could 'save the land for the children', at which the child innocently asks 'is there a happy ending?' More controversial still was *No Pressure*, a short film made by star director and writer Richard Curtis for the UK-based 10:10 campaign group. The short film, made for the web, was intended to spoof hectoring greens. It depicted schoolchildren being blown up, requiring vast quantities of horror movie blood, when they refused to act on climate change.

These adverts may have been aimed at adults, using images of children, but many of the complaints centred on the idea that climate change might scare children. Indeed, there is some research to suggest young people are concerned, though this can be spun in a variety of ways. For example, a recent Unicef report on a poll of UK children, stressed youthful concern about climate change and was tied to pressure on the government to increase coverage of the issue in schools (Carrington, 2013). On the other hand, there is Bjørn Lomborg (2009) chastising campaigners for 'frightening children with exaggerations', and claims that young people need to learn abstracted scientific principles not 'issues' (Shepherd, 2011). Prominent US climate scientist James Hansen has written a book for adults entitled *Storms of My Grandchildren* and is clearly happy to refer to children in order to talk to adults. However he too suggests that you can't tell children about climate change because it is too scary. Rather, Hansen suggests working to help re-connect young people with nature so they are better prepared to deal with the issue (Hansen, 2013).

Written by one generation for the next, cultural products aimed at children are almost always about what adults think children should and can know. They can be deeply anxious and sometimes conflicted; futuristic, in that they wonder what type of world the reader will grow up into, but also nostalgic as authors think about their own childhood; full of guilt and pride about what sort of world we will be leaving, along with fears and hope for the future. But the actual child can be quite absent. One of the more interesting media studies to unpick this issue considered the 1990s boom in environmental coverage. Rather than simply interviewing young people about their reactions to environmental television, David Gauntlett invited them to make their own videos, and studied how they went about this (Gauntlett, 1996).

Superheroes

Comparing the 1990s boom in green youth literature with the more recent mid-2000s one, one of the striking themes to emerge was the use and re-use of superhero characters. Some might turn their nose up at these characters. Who needs a superhero to save us? If we find a 'great man' view distasteful when applied to history, why make use of it when considering futures? We need to find ways of talking about mass, cooperative action, not some magic pseudo-religious superhero saviour from the sky. But — looking at the books — these eco-superheroes are quite diverse (gender aside). Certainly some of the books are quite patronising. But others are more knowing, either laughing at the idea of a saviour or seeing the hero as a composite of action of the masses.

Flying far above all eco-superheroes stories is TV star, Captain Planet. As the theme tune repeatedly told viewers, 'He's a hero, gonna take pollution down to zero'. Created by Ted Turner and Barbara Pyle, *Captain Planet and the Planeteers* ran on UK and US television from 1990 to 1996 and is still syndicated today. The basic patterning of the series was based on the premise that Gaia 'the spirit of the Earth' was, with a nod to James Lovelock, awakened by human destruction of the planet. She sent five magic rings to young people across the globe; these 'Planeteers' were then equipped to fight environmental destruction and, occasionally, social injustice. There was a memorable episode which tackled peace in the West Bank, South Africa and Northern Ireland. If the Planeteers faced a particularly tough foe, they could pool their magic rings to create the superhero character of Captain Planet. Thus, the caped crusader flew in to assist us, but as a booming voiceover reminded audiences within every episode, it is only 'by your powers combined' that change really happens.

It's not just Americans who apply superheroes to green issues. Take, for example, Jonathon Porritt's 1991 large full-colour hardback, *Captain Eco and the Fate of the Earth*. Again, perhaps as a nod to Lovelock, we're told Captain Eco comes from the Earth but is angry with the way humans are mistreating it. After being introduced to Clive (aged 9) and Michelle (aged 12), Captain Eco exclaims 'Suffering Solar Systems! If these are 'standard' earthlings, no wonder the Earth's in such trouble'. He then flies around wagging his finger at everyone for being lazy or stupid, with Clive and Michelle scolded for being more interested in books, television, sleeping, music and football than the environment. Whereas Captain Planet was powered by the collaborative action of young people (albeit in response to a supernatural force) in *Captain Eco* the child characters are the audience for a superhero lecture.

Fast forward to 2000 and, as earnest as the original Captain Planet, there is the US publication *Understanding Global Warming with Max Axiom, Super Scientist*. Max is a muscle-bound (and not always fully clothed) character who, after being struck by lightning, is inspired to travel the world collecting degrees in as many subjects as possible to become a 'Super Scientist'. His lab coat allows him to travel through time and space, he has X-ray sunglasses and the ability to shrink to the size of an atom. Other books in the Max Axiom series cover photosynthesis, bacteria, sound or light. Importantly perhaps, here the heroism is less about saving the planet, and more about the adventure of finding out.

Your Planet Needs You! A Kid's Guide to Going Green by Dave Reay (2009) takes a very different approach, and this is where I think the narrative gets a bit more interesting. Here the superhero character Maximus is called upon from space by politicians but, with very British tongue in cheek, he is constructed as possessing more glamour than intelligence and has to turn to a group of young people to understand the problem of global warming. They take him to their climate club where the source of knowledge is the science teacher, Miss Weatherbottom. The superhero here is a joke, as well as a straight man to whom explanations can be directed (thus Maximus plays the role children often have in such books). In a similar vein, *George Saves the World by Lunchtime* by Jo Readman (2006) features a small child dressing up as a superhero, making small changes around the home. *Michael Recycle* by Ellie Bethel (2008) uses a similar device, deploying a superhero who flies down from the sky, but is represented as a child playing at dressing up, with a colander as a helmet. Change is enacted in this case by people in the polluted town in question talking to one another and forging connections.

In these last three books, the superhero guise is a bit of a joke, domesticated and made juvenile, with a knowing play upon saviour narratives. They laugh at the earnestness of the 1990s and yet seem to revel in the basic narrative too. Perhaps they are best described as having their superhero and eating it. Looking at this collection of eco superheroes, there's one striking omission: a clearly articulated villain. Some locate blame with human stupidity or laziness but the prime source of the threats is usually vague. The closest we get to anything concrete is *Captain Planet*, though even this features a cohort of baddies symbolizing a range of problems such as misapplied, uncaring science or reckless business as well as characteristics such as greed, gluttony or hate. (Interestingly, nuclear power is included as an example.) In a few episodes the villains even join forces in an echo of the composite powers behind Captain Planet to make an alter ego, Captain Pollution.

Environmental problems have multi-causal, complex explanations, even on the Cartoon Network. Whether the lack of baddies is because such stories accurately depict the abstract nature of climate change or more simply because media producers are too nervous to point fingers at people who might advertise with them, I'm not sure. It might also reflect an approach to climate communication which focuses on the positive actions people can take. One might argue fantasy super-villain characters devolve public responsibility as much as the idea of a saviour from the sky, so perhaps it is for the best that they don't feature much.

The political economies of children's green media
There is an interesting question about the materiality of much of this media. That eco superhero Hall of Fame is built out of a pile of dead trees while telling kids to recycle. A recent 'eco' reprint of 1971 classic *The Lorax* was produced on 100% recycled paper because the 'Lorax loves trees and so do we', somehow managing to forget that we might be better off just picking up a second-hand copy. There is also the infrastructure of the bookshop to consider (air conditioning, etc.) not to mention all those never-read books picked up on a 3-4-2 deal. Books have become a disposable product. 'Healthy Planet' bookshops are stocked with books saved from landfill offered for free (Campbell, 2011).

One of the many ironies is that despite its apparent relationship with a particular thread of Romanticism which privileges the outdoors over shopping, children's literature as a product has been a force in consumer capitalism — which is, arguably, part of the problem. The *New York Times* might complain that children's books tend to cast consumers as villains, but the Romantic spirit has long helped sell things (see Campbell, 1987), in bookselling as much as anywhere else (Wright, 2005). This is perhaps especially true when it comes to children's books, be this piles of Harry Potters, the purchasing of a 'classic' (or edgy new science fiction for that matter) to express a form of identity, cross branding and spin-off toys or topping up formal education through revision primers. Arguably, the types of consumption at work here, including its apparent discontinuities, intersect with twenty-first century green consumerism very neatly, as it can be a form of middle-class performance through consumption, even via the shunning of other products.

In 2005, Greenpeace ran a campaign comparing the international publishers of *Harry Potter and the Half-Blood Prince* in terms of their use of sustainable fibre (Greenpeace International, 2005). There was a mini-movement towards ecologically sustainable publishing around that time. Random House publicly committed itself to making its book production 'Ancient Forest Friendly', and Leo

Hickman insisted his ethical living book (published by Eden Project Books) was printed on recycled paper, using vegetable inks (Crown, 2005). Egmont Press not only decided to source their paper carefully, but encouraged other UK publishers to do the same, sharing knowledge about wood-pulp sources across the industry. It promoted this move with a reprint of Michael Morpurgo's *Kensuke's Kingdom*, a story about a boy shipwrecked on an island, on paper approved by the Forest Stewardship Council (FSC). Morpurgo noted in a preface: 'next time you're looking for a book or your parents are buying furniture, think of Kensuke and look for the FSC logo', offering a nice example of the environmentalist message of the book being directly linked to its materiality.

Green has long been a marketable property in the consumer cultures of children's media. (The BBC publication, the annual *Blue Peter Green Book*, is actually orange in colour, on account of carrying the logo of its supermarket sponsor, Sainsbury's.) It isn't just books. The Reverend Billy Talen (2013) makes jokes about 'Drowning Elmo' toys to keep us entertained while the tsunamis and flash floods 'bounced on the horizon like Loony Tunes'. But when the climate change and energy galleries at the Science Museum are sponsored by Shell and BP respectively, do we really need such satire? There are even anti-pollution sweets, or 'smog ball' sours (see toxicwastecandy.com). At the 2013 Royal Society summer exhibition a stall on energy gave out slices of seaside rock with the words 'solar energy' running through yellow discs (I think they were meant to represent the sun). At the Big Bang Fair, British Nuclear Fuels Ltd (BNFL) also offered sticks of rock, apparently to symbolise nuclear rods (Bell, 2013a).

It's hard to see what impact sponsorship has on content, but it is striking that the Sainsbury's *Blue Peter Green Book* has notes on green consumerism, but manages to avoid too much discussion of cutting consumption, just as the Shell-sponsored *Climate Stories* exhibition at the Science Museum avoids prominent reference to oil and gas. There are also more direct forms of campaigning, without the need for sponsored mediators. A fracking themed colouring book featuring 'Talisman Terry, your friendly Fracosaurus' (Hickman, 2011) was speedily withdrawn as a giveaway for county fairs after being mocked on US television (Miller, 2011) but other resources have been more resilient to critique. There's the online game *Richie's World Of Adventure* which, courtesy of nuclear enrichment company, Urenco, invites players to pick up energy orbs releasing 'facts' such as how reliable and safe nuclear energy is. On the other side, there's Greenpeace's equivalent, *Duke Anti-Nuke* where part of the aim of the game is to dodge publicity agents. Such materials might seem funny, but raise a larger issue: when we privatised our energy system, did we also privatise the public engagement with energy, and is that okay? These kinds of communications point to a segmentation of our energy imaginations, meaning we talk of wind, gas, nuclear or solar in isolation, not low carbon as a whole. It may also serve to segment audiences casting them as customers not citizens.

Happy endings

Captains Planet and Eco, Michael Recycle and the Science Museum's climate change gallery are merely the stories adults offer to young people. They may be offered ready-made, but they can be re-made by their audiences too. I'd like to conclude by celebrating participatory and reflexive environmental communication. Between 1973 and 1994 the BBC broadcast a children's television show: *Why Don't You Just Switch Off Your Television Set and Go and Do Something Less Boring Instead?* Putting aside the 'Auntie Beeb' (national broadcaster) ideas that television should be rationed for young people and that the outdoors is somehow healthy, there is a message in this apparently self-critical media stance. It is arguably much easier to make in the cultural and technological context of online communications and digital media (see also Gauntlett, 2011; Jenkins, 2006). Get making for yourself. Hack. Blog. Occupy media culture. Run your own discussion events. Offer alternative tours of museums, either in real space or through podcasts (e.g. www.tateatate.org). Heckle literature with comment cards left in books in libraries and bookshops. Follow UN negotiators (e.g. www.adoptanegotiator.org). Tear up your syllabus and invite teachers to work with you to produce something more sustainable instead (e.g. www.post-crasheconomics.com).

We can get beyond adults making media for children, or even young people responding with media of their own. Children are, all too often, seen and not heard when it comes to environmental issues: they are recipients of knowledge or even simply symbols of a future requiring protection in campaigns aimed at adults. That's not to say older generations should not offer their knowledge to young people: we should draw on the hard-won wisdom of the past and present. Neither do I want to — in Jacqueline Rose's words — set the child up as the site of a lost truth. The framing of climate change as an issue of inter-generational justice can serve to pit one age against another. It is relevant to note that the very idea of a separate youth culture which rejects previous generations was to some extent a construction that segmented markets in order to sell more specific products to teenagers (Kinder, 1995). There is more to be gained from building multi-generation stories that splice together the wit and wisdom of the past, present and future.

Or we can give out sweeties at the Big Bang Fair.

Cautionary tales: The Sky is Falling! The World is Ending!

Renata Tyszczuk

Cautionary tales are meant to warn us against acts of transgression or recklessness, like the 'be careful what you wish for' or 'shouldn't have gone into the woods' narratives familiar from fairy tales, or those exaggerated stories about not heeding instructions (or of taking one too many risks) from Heinrich Hoffmann's *Der Struwwelpeter* (1845) or the 'awful warnings' of 'bad behaviour' in Hilaire Belloc's *Cautionary Tales for Children* (1907). These are tales about situations that go beyond some boundary and unsettle the status quo, or simply get you into serious trouble. Cautionary tales expose the dangers, taboos and prohibitions of certain courses of action. They tell how the performance of a forbidden act, a violation of rules or disregard of caution can lead to an unpleasant fate. Cautionary tales delight and astound in narrating the disastrous consequences of a particular turn of events. Remember 'Matilda, Who told Lies and was Burned to Death'?

Cautionary tales range from fables containing cross-species dressing — wolves that can be mistaken for grandmothers or sheep — to genre-crossing environmental parables and crisis narratives of conditional forecasts and ruptures where the world is doomed to end and the sky keeps falling. These are all stories with a twist, a shock, a surprise and calamity; and with a 'sting in the tale'. Fears flourish in such stories. Stories are our way of trying to make sense of it all and bringing a sense of wonder to the proceedings. In an uncertain and fearsome world, cautionary tales are here to stay.

We are compelled to tell stories about our nightmares just as much as our dreams. Cautionary tales have accompanied us through the fears and paranoias of the last century of anthropogenic calamity, exploring the unknowable and thinking the unthinkable. We have turned to stories to work through the consequences of pollution and toxicity, confront nuclear threats and the cold war, deal with environmental distress and inbalances and imagine devastated cities and catastrophic climate change, all in the context of our own turbulent tendencies. In Rachel Carson's *Silent Spring* (1962), the innocently titled prologue, 'A Fable for Tomorrow', warned about the use of pesticides by weaving a poetic narrative about seasonal dysfunction and desolation. Environmental apocalypse was imagined in Harry Harrison's novel *Make Room, Make Room!* (1966) and the film it inspired, *Soylent Green* (1973), while the worst-case scenarios of nuclear war developed by Herman Kahn with the Rand Corporation set the scene for Stanley Kubrick's satirical *Dr Strangelove* (1964). Such cautionary tales negotiate the discord between the actual and the (im)possible and test the pragmatic, moral, physical and, at times, unexpected consequences of certain courses of action. They propel us to imagine how things could be — disastrously — otherwise. Ultimately therefore, cautionary tales can be a strategy for dealing with the contingent fictions of our own making.

We live in an uncertain world fraught with potential danger and imminent collapse. 2013 was yet another year of extreme weather, epic floods, seismic unrest, typhoons, pestilence and war. Fear and foreboding are appropriate responses to the prospect of catastrophic climate disruption and we have cautionary tales of grim futures in abundance. New titles on the bookshelves add to the increasing array of future disaster tales warning of climate change, of a world that is 'post-apocalyptic', 'post-human' or 'without us', along with user manuals for coping with 'the-end-of-the world-as-we-know-it.' These by now familiar narratives of doom and gloom have tended not to provoke action. But stories that warn us to take heed or act differently on an increasingly densely urbanised, energy intensive and chronically convulsive planet are surely important cautionary tales to listen to. And, if our fossil-fuelled cities and their dependant hinterlands are at greatest risk from the impacts and consequences of climate change then perhaps we still need some cautionary tales at the ready.

A thousand and one cautionary tales
What cautionary tales should we tell for a planet of cities in planetary crisis? Biblical, mythical, historical and recent scientific accounts all relate how ancient cities were extremely vulnerable to flood, drought, plague as well as a shaking ground. The collapse of ancient urban civilisations is regularly attributed to climatic and geophysical disruptions. But the situation is considered all the more urgent as the shifts in earth systems we are experiencing now are not only rare in the Earth's 4.6 billion-year history but have never occured before on such a tightly packed and densely occupied planet.

But the places we live in and the lifestyles we indulge in on our planetary-scaled construction site are remarkably stubborn when it comes to being dislodged by planetary turbulence. The settlements we have inherited, the burgeoning sprawl and megacities we are rushing to build and the shrinking, exhausted postindustrial towns all have the capacity to bounce back or cling on — or indeed ignore all warnings when it comes to climate change. There are plenty of stories about cities that take us to hell and back, situated as they often are in the path of cyclones, hurricanes, pests and at the mercy of drought, earthquakes and floods. Alongside narratives of tyranny and prophecy there are stories of folly and avoidable calamity as well as tales of improbable endurance. Making it through to the next retelling is something cities do well. Telling stories to survive, just as Scheherazade does in *A Thousand and One Nights*, is a constant theme for cities and city dwellers. And, like the stories she tells, each of those stories undergoes myriad retellings and generates further stories, alarming and compelling in equal measure. We are not held in suspense by any sense of ending, but by the *storytelling*. Cities, like stories, are provisional, capable of constant revision and reinvention. Cities are unfinished stories.

We live and breathe stories. We tell stories in order to make sense of the beginnings, middles and ends of our lives. We seek out narratives that can reassure, cajole, entertain, provoke, persuade or demand action. They sustain us or allow us to linger on. Stories matter. But in the context of climate change and the unstable planetary conditions we find ourselves living in, how do we tell stories that might make a difference? The distinctive features of climate change, its pervasiveness, uncertainty, interdependency, historicity, interdisciplinarity and temporality (Smith, 2011) affect every aspect of human lives, politics and culture. Climate change is too here, too there, too everywhere, too weird, too much, too big, too everything. Climate change is not a story that can be told in itself, but rather, it is now the condition for any story that might be told about cities, or our inhabitation of this fractious planet.

Tales from the Anthropocene

We live in an unsettled time. And we are unsettled by the relationship with the world that we find ourselves in, and the new knowledge that our species appears to be changing it, probably for the worse, and at a planetary scale. In a sense we are living in a cautionary tale of our own making. The Anthropocene, or 'the Age of Humans', is the name proposed for the geological epoch we find ourselves in. It has superseded the 'safe' and relatively stable Holocene (Zalasiewicz et al., 2009). The International Commission on Stratigraphy and the International Union of Geological Sciences are currently in the midst of a long process to find evidence for the new geological stratum named after us. This temporal moment in the strata coincides with the particular historical juncture that has seen predictions of human-induced climatic tipping points and extinction events. In addition to the build-up of greenhouse gases, the new geological stratum is to be defined by human landscape transformations exceeding natural sediment production; by the acidification of oceans; by the relentless destruction of biota, and above all by radical instability. But it is the accelerated growth of cities that is the most characteristic geophysical feature of the so-called Anthropocene-in-the-making. As the philosopher Michel Serres has noted, 'When it is unevenly distributed, skyrocketing demographic growth becomes concentrated and stuck together in giant units, colossal banks of humanity, as powerful as oceans, deserts or icecaps, themselves stockpiles of ice, heat, dryness, or water' (Serres, 1995: 17).

The massive destructive potential of our accumulated activities, whether intentional or not, promises to be ever more stratigraphically significant in the future. Jan Zalasiewicz, who convenes the Anthropocene Working Group for the International Commission on Stratigraphy and the International Union of Geological Sciences, has also written a fictional narrative, *The Earth After Us* (2008). This cautionary tale, set 100 million years from now, imagines alien forensic geologists of the future finding urban traces and remnants of a long extinguished human history in the rocks. But the tale also brings to light the actual challenges facing stratigraphers in attempting to define an epoch by anticipating human-induced geological event horizons of a magnitude and timescale difficult to comprehend. A science and practice that usually follows the evidence, stratigraphy is immersed in the speculative world of conjectures, in the identification of evidence before it is preserved in the rocks, in the manner of 'precrime' in the science fiction tale *The Minority Report* (Philip K. Dick, 1956) and in the rhetorical upside-down world of the thought experiment.

The identification of the Anthropocene positions humans as the fossil-fuelled driving force of change, capable of epochal shifts, but at the same time undermines all human constructions by warning us of our own eventual fossilization. Geological time frames may remind us that all building is provisional but global urban practices show little recognition of the precarious interdependence of human and non-human worlds and their radical instability. The question here is how to tell new stories about how we design, build and maintain enduring cities, structures and communities on the Earth's surface even if, unwittingly, in the grandest of narratives, we might have already written ourselves out of the story.

The story of climate change is the changing story of the human species' attachment to Earth. It is a story that veers between precarious inhabitation of, and ruthless opportunism on, a stranger-than-fiction planet. With our accidental and unsettling advance into the Anthropocene, stories with the planetary at stake — the earth-shattering, sky-falling and world-ending variety — have renewed poignancy. Catastrophic events involve the collision of times and scales that are incommensurable: geological time folding into gestures and routines of everyday social life, the global invading the local, planetary energy bearing down on a city. Cautionary tales that bring in the cosmic scale are ripe for re-telling. They draw attention to the transformative power of stories — where things might change, or remain the same... *or else...*

The sky is falling!

This is a tale that brings the cosmic down to earth. 'The Sky Is Falling', better known as 'Chicken Licken', 'Henny Penny' or 'Chicken Little' is an old cumulative fable about a chicken who runs around panicking that the sky is falling. The phrase, 'the sky is falling', has passed into the English language as a common idiom indicating a hysterical or mistaken belief that disaster is imminent. Hence its ready association with the doom-ridden predictions of *Limits to Growth* (1972) (see Meadows, 1999) and crisis narratives that deliver shrill announcements of runaway, unprecedented or catastrophic climate change. But it also warns us of the unfortunate consequences of telling a story in one way — it makes it all too easy to dismiss well-meaning 'doom-sayers' even if their story must be told again and again.

There are of course many versions of the original fable, but the main premise is that a chicken overreacts to a random event — an acorn falling on her head

— and thinks the sky is about to fall and the world will end. The panicky chicken rushes to tell the authorities, the King or, in some versions, the President. On her journey she persuades other farmyard animals, Henny Penny, Cocky Lockey and Goosey Loosey to join her in the mission. But, with all the running around worrying about the sky falling, the chicken forgets to avoid other threats and usually ends up as supper for the unscrupulous Foxy Loxy. What the sundry versions of the tale have in common is that the sky doesn't fall and the world never quite ends. But in a runaway mixed-up world, it always depends on the particular version of events, and as Margaret Atwood's re-telling of the tale reminds us, it is always possible to interrupt the narrative chain: 'That's one analysis, said Turkey Lurkey. But there's data to show it isn't the sky that's falling. It's the earth that's rising' (Atwood, 2006:67).

Global warming scare stories: is the sky really falling?
The tale lends itself well to various cautionary political and societal tales and the moral can be adjusted accordingly. In some versions, the intended moral is not to be a 'chicken', but to have the courage of your convictions. In other versions it can be interpreted as a warning of jumping to conclusions too quickly, of mass hysteria as well as the potential for others to manipulate the resulting runaway situation to their own ends. The most common allusion to Chicken Little currently is as a critical metaphor for environmental extremists or 'eco-loons', and global warming alarmists, or 'warmists'. The 'sky is falling' has become a by-word for scaremongering or doom-ridden campaigning rhetoric, and in turn generates its own headline-grabbing rejoinders: 'Chicken Little Warns Of The Sky Falling Continuously. Maybe One Day, We'll Learn To Ignore Him' (http://musingsofamadconservative.blogspot.co.uk 3 September 2013). Contemporary news media relies on the push and pull of accusations, the mock creation of partisan lines and fake controversies in the climate change debate, in turn spurring the libertarian instincts of climate contrarians. Here, an online commentator going by the name of 'SouthOhioGipper' responds to an article by Andrew Winston ('Obama Gave a Monumental Climate Change Speech, But It's Still Not Enough') in the *Harvard Business Review*:

> Sorry, I don't look at the weather and see some angry Earth mother goddess ready to destroy mankind. The hysteria over Carbon is just that... HYSTERIA. It is a million chicken little's screaming that the sky is falling and I'm sick of hearing it.
>
> Carbon is NOT a pollutant, it is NOT a toxin and people like you are sheep willing to sign away their freedom, prosperity and lives in the HOPE of changing the weather, without even a metric standard by which you could judge the efficacy.
>
> I am not going to allow the economic freedom of myself or any other American, rich, poor or otherwise to be dictated to by debunked malthusians and AGW hysterics and paranoid maniacs. Which is exactly as I see you.

Environmentalism is being used by anti-capitalists around the world to attack what is left of America's free market capitalism in the hopes of weakening America further and reducing the quality of life of its citizens. (Winston, 2013)

Elements from the Chicken Little story parallel the charges commonly levelled against climate change narratives: the use of scare tactics, or of rousing emotions of fear and anxiety, as well as the simplistic use of false dichotomy. In Chicken Little's story we are presented from the outset with a false dichotomy — either the sky is falling or Chicken Little is wrong. However, what the canny fox, or the thoughtful turkey realise is that there are always other possibilities, detours, endings and even digestifs in any story. And, in a tumble-down world, as Atwood's activist Chicken Little would argue with her detractors, there are always other ways of looking at it:

'The sky is falling' is a metaphor, said Chicken Little huffily. It's true that the sky really is falling, but the falling of the sky represents all sorts of other things that are falling as well. Falling down, and falling apart. You should wake up! (Atwood, 2006)

The sky is falling! We must tell the President!
So much for the wake-up call. But what if the President is fast getting a reputation as the 'sky-is-falling-president'? And if that is the case, who can the President tell? Currently, if you do a search engine query for the phrase 'the sky is falling', there are plenty of media references, including tweets, cartoons and news articles about US President Obama as either the 'sky-is-falling-president' or the 'Chicken-Little-president'. Previously this accolade for 'warming hysteria' went to Al Gore or James Hansen. Repeated warnings of greater risk of severe weather events to governments and authorities have had hardly any impact on the global political economy of energy and there is growing recognition that aggressive rhetoric emphasising fear of environmental collapse is unlikely to make a difference. This was the context that Hurricane Sandy blew through. Its devastation of New York's coastline had its own agency in putting climate change back on the agenda. On 29 October 2012, Hurricane Sandy breached the seawall in Battery Park City. Floodwaters gushed into New York's five boroughs, submerging cars, tunnels and the subway and plunging skyscrapers and neighbourhoods into darkness. The hurricane was a weather system of 'historic proportions', killing at least 159 people, destroying or damaging more than 650,000 homes and costing the state an estimated $65 billion in emergency response and recovery efforts.

In his 'climate change' speech in June 2013, Obama delivered a different kind of cautionary tale. He was at pains not only to debunk so-called 'sceptical' views on anthropogenic global warming but also to make climate change urgent and everybody's business:

Now, we know that no single weather event is caused solely by climate change. Droughts and fires and floods, they go back to ancient times. But we also know that in a world that's warmer than it used to be, all weather events are affected by a warming planet. The fact that sea levels in New York, in New York Harbor, are now a foot higher than a century ago — that didn't cause Hurricane Sandy, but it certainly contributed to the destruction that left large parts of our mightiest city dark and underwater.... And we know that the costs of these events can be measured in lost lives and lost livelihoods, lost homes, lost businesses, hundreds of billions of dollars in emergency services and disaster relief. In fact, those who are already feeling the effects of climate change don't have time to deny it — they're busy dealing with it.... We need to act. We don't have time for a meeting of the Flat Earth Society. (Obama, 2013)

So not exactly 'the sky is falling', but there is plenty to worry about. Threats to our 'mightiest cities' abound. Hurricane Sandy's unprecedented storm surge revealed how lack of preparation in a crowded city can intensify any disaster. Moreover, vulnerability to disaster in cities is exacerbated by the economic and political pressures that drive the less privileged to cluster in especially perilous zones.

And when infrastructure fails, much that is usually invisible or taken for granted is made visible: power relations, as well as socio-material or technological relations. But even if we acknowledge present-day costs of such disasters we are still not very good at assessing risks and benefits for a far away climate-changed future. Planning for resilience requires cities and their infrastructures not only to be prepared for any threat but also to have the ability to absorb, recover or adapt to disasters. Even so, surprising things can happen in cities at the worst of times. Occupy Sandy's relief effort was in the immediate term more effective than any top-down response. It worked on the ground in the aftermath of the storm with supply chains and support networks established by the Occupy movement.

But 'being prepared' can also mean protecting the city from itself, from civil unrest and the perceived challenges to the status quo. It bears acknowledging that renewed attention to narratives of 'disaster preparedness' and 'hazard prevention' has arisen in a context where the Pentagon has been warned to stand guard against 'climate surprises' and the potential for a cascade of catastrophic events that could put 'America at risk' (Goldenberg, 2012). The 'Fix and Fortify' poster that appears prominently round New York reveals that in many places the defensive measures being taken for recovery are far from finished.

We have nothing to fear *but* the sky falling
The 'sky is falling' can be both a causal and moral tale of panic and folly. But it can also be a story about the very real dangers of living as a quarrelsome species

on a disaster-prone planet. And yet it bears remembering that there is an unruliness in the human experience of the sky above our heads — the changing and unpredictable weather — which undermines any global project for climate preservation, manipulation and control of even good behaviour. Our hopes and fears, our predictions and even our prejudices can't stop the sky from falling but there are plenty of other things we could be getting on with. Most narratives about climate change have been framed in terms of trying to stop the future happening and of struggling to avert the myriad catastrophes that threaten our age. This type of thinking has produced anxiety, frustration and may even have served to further embed inaction. Perhaps instead we should take heed and listen to the wise words of Chief Vitalstatistix in Goscinny and Uderzo's *Asterix the Gaul* series: '*We have nothing to fear but the sky falling on our heads*'. The seemingly preposterous and superstitious Gaullish fears are now traced back to a largely verifiable comet impact that took place sometime between 465 and 200 BCE. So the sky has fallen and we should be prepared for the next time. The plucky Chicken Little and the fearless Chief Vitalstatistix remind us that anything could happen — and it probably will. The sky falling is *everything* we have to worry about, for on Earth, chaos ensues, variability prevails, change is to be expected. As Michel Serres writes,

> So, the stone falls on the city, the earth quakes and thus shakes our walls and our constructed certainties; nature bursts in on the citizen, who believes only in the assurances provided by human labor and by the political order or police... We ought to admire the madness or wisdom of our ancestors the Gauls, who feared, it is told, that the sky would fall on their heads: indeed, that could happen this morning, unannounced, and what's more it will surely happen some fine morning. Their madness or wisdom is just like ours, alive and brief, the eternal anguish of the king in hell, threatened by the rock. (Serres,1995: 72)

The World is ending!
This is a true story. It is about a city that succumbs to earth-shattering forces. On the morning of 1 November, All Saints Day, 1755, the world ended in Lisbon. The city was rocked by three huge tremors that opened giant fissures in the ground, destroying countless buildings including most of the churches, monasteries, convents, and the Royal Palace. The earthquake caught a large proportion of the populace worshipping in the churches, which collapsed onto congregations. Fires swept through the city, ignited, according to some accounts, by toppling altar candles. The survivors struggled to reach the waterfront where they were met with the terrifying sight of a withdrawing sea exposing a world littered with the tangled debris of shipwrecks. The tsunamis that followed overwhelmed the city. Many spared by the water perished in the fires which raged in the city for a further five days.

In the second half of the eighteenth century Lisbon's destruction came to be considered as the most momentous event since the fall of the Roman Empire (Neiman, 2002: 240). Numerous accounts of the disaster were published all over Europe. These ranged from cathartic testimony and apocalyptic sermons through to scientific and philosophical exploration and make-believe. With its intricate mix of myth, fable and history, Voltaire's satirical narrative *Candide, ou l'Optimisme*, was a cautionary tale on the current state of the world with the headline-grabbing destruction of Lisbon providing a significant episode.

> Scarcely had they set foot in the city, still weeping over the death of their benefactor, than they felt the earth quake beneath their feet. In the port a boiling sea rose up and smashed the ships lying at anchor. Whirlwinds of flame and ash covered the streets and public squares: houses disintegrated, roofs were upended upon foundations, and foundations crumbled. Thirty thousand inhabitants of both sexes and all ages were crushed beneath the ruins... *'The end of the world is come!'* Candide shouted. (Voltaire, 1759)

Voltaire was as horrified by the earthquake as by the purges that followed. (Neiman, 2002: 324). The Inquisition's response to the calamity was an *auto-da-fé*, an 'act of faith', designed to prevent the wrath of God and further catastrophe. Sinners and heretics were rounded up for public execution in what remained of the city's squares. Candide and his philosopher-master Pangloss get caught up in the disaster and its philosophical and theological repercussions. And while Pangloss is being hanged for heresy, the earth shakes again and Candide weeps: 'If this is the best of all possible worlds, what are the others like?' (Voltaire, 1759).

Cosmic madness

The Lisbon quake wiped out a major European city. This unsettled everybody just at the moment when the Enlightenment subject was emerging. It is often presented as the first 'modern' disaster prompting philosophy to provide rational explanations of natural catastrophes. Voltaire's 'Poème sur le désastre de Lisbonne' (1756), written just after the earthquake, questioned the Leibnizian notion of a benevolent deity supervising the 'best of all possible worlds'. No one could doubt the uselessness of humans when it came to the threatening forces of the earth. And as Nigel Clark writes, 'Lisbon's concatenation of horrors signaled not only physical and corporeal annihilation but the collapse of a way of making sense of the event itself' (Clark, 2011: 90). And it has been troubling us ever since. Thank goodness then, for the human capacity for satire and irony, as Julian Barnes notes in his reflection on *Candide*:

> The world is not reformed by the end of *Candide*, and cultivating one's garden protects no one from an army of Bulgars. Satire is not about 'finding a solution', doesn't spring from a worked-out strategy for the micro-managed moral rehabilitation of humanity; rather, it is the necessary expression of

moral rage. Satirists are by nature pessimists; they know that the world changes all too slowly. If satire worked — if the hypocrite and liar, publicly chastised, reformed themselves — then satire would no longer be needed. "But to what end," Candide muses, "was the world formed?" Martin replies: "To make us mad." Satire is one response to, and outlet for, this *cosmic madness*. (Barnes, 2011)

The Lisbon earthquake showed all too well the workings of a violent recalcitrant world and the fallibility of humans. The extreme events in Lisbon presaged the end of theological interpretations of disaster but also challenged the idea of a purely natural disaster and introduced the politicization of disasters (Huet, 2012). It suggested that the responsibility for widespread destruction could be held by humans — and, according to Rousseau, lessons could be learnt from the overcrowded city on how to both think and construct differently (Rousseau, 1756). In the aftermath of the earthquake, the Marquis of Pombal took charge of the relief and reconstruction efforts, setting up office in his carriage among the ruins. The army was mobilized to enforce the rebuilding work and help in the organization of food, water and burials. Tents and huts were erected for streams of homeless refugees and the royal court was accommodated in a huge complex of tents and pavilions in the hills of Ajuda. Rubble was cleared, bodies were hastily buried at sea, surveys of seismic activity carried out and seismically protected buildings were constructed. Everything possible was done to confirm Lisbon's ability to survive and recover even if the King himself, obviously shaken by the events, chose never to leave his tent again. Kant's detailed accounts of the earthquake, credited as the beginnings of modern seismology, pondered the 'inconstancy of the world' and offered the reflection that '[m]an was not born to build everlasting cottages upon this stage of vanity' (Kant, 1756).

Aftershocks

Cities are at greatest risk from the impacts of climate change. No matter what the origins of a disaster, it is human systems — physical, cultural, political — that can amplify, channel, mitigate or transform what happens next. It is well known that it is collapsing buildings and ineffectual infrastructures that cause the loss of life in hazardous situations and not only the workings of a fractious earth. Ever since the Lisbon earthquake we have been acutely aware that cities amplify the effects of episodic planetary turbulence by stacking large populations in heavy brittle structures (Clark, 2003:190; Rousseau, 1756). In spite of all our contemporary efforts with early warning systems, seismic safety codes, risk registers and plans for civil emergencies, the cities that we continue to build to accommodate the mass of humans on a dynamic planet will always be the places that are most susceptible to planetary disruptions. And in the context of rapidly accelerating urbanization and the complex interweaving of weather, lives, infrastructures and economies it is often the fissures between governments and civil society that are made more evident when disaster strikes.

The earth sciences have offered us explanations for the wavering and turbulent nature of the earth and suggest that such catastrophes and convulsions as the Lisbon earthquake, capable of upsetting all human creations and constructions, are but minor readjustments of a planet in constant motion. But in spite of better scientific understanding of the shaky ground we dwell on, for the most part we have continued to assume or hope for the solidity and stability of the earth beneath our feet. And we are not much better now then we were after Lisbon's disaster at making sense of it all. Recent narratives around the Anthropocene have resonance with the impact of the Lisbon earthquake in terms of the scale of cultural shift involved in readjusting to increasingly volatile urban conditions. We are now starting to acknowledge the earth-moving, sky-falling effects of a human-natural-planetary hybrid system and the cultural, philosophical and political aftershocks.

Cautionary tales for the Anthropocene remind us that we are always within an earth-shattering, sky-falling nature. Nature is not just something that acts on us or we act on it. It is our cosmic madness and our cosmic wisdom. So there are plenty of reasons to be afraid. We need cautionary tales, and not just for sounding the alarm or announcing the end of the world. They can also be about stock-taking. They can help us acknowledge the complexity of the human condition bound up as it is with cosmic upheavals, planetary scale adjustments, resource poverty, inadequate evacuation plans and infrastructure breakdown. Cautionary tales also allow for emotions and human aptitudes to be explored, including distress, even wit, humour and ingenuity in the face of it all. They can help to reappraise responsibility and relate the many different ways in which societies take climate change into account when they make their own plans for the future and the different stories they choose to tell. Climate change in its pervasiveness will necessarily be part of all future stories.

Pre-cautionary tales
The 'precautionary principle' was written into the story in the Rio Declaration at the 1992 Earth Summit. Usually understood as a version of 'better safe than sorry', the Rio formulation of the principle in the context of climate change states that, 'where there are threats to serious or irreversible damage, lack of full scientific certainty shall not be used as a reason for postponing cost-effective measures to prevent environmental degradation.' It has provoked recent debate and much handwringing on the place of risk and uncertainty in the context of policy decisions on climate change (Bell, 2013b). It was summoned recently by Yeb Sano's heartfelt plea for action at COP19 in the wake of Typhoon Haiyan's devastation of the Philippines on 8 November 2013.

The precautionary principle does not simply urge caution or inaction in the face of unknowns although this is how it is usually understood. Indeed it fractures the (often illusory) connection between scientific (un)certainty and political action: for it asserts that even in the absence of certainty decisions can be taken. Furthermore, a precautionary approach invites consideration of what it means to take action as well as the consequences of any action. It thus calls up a duty of care and social responsibility but also 'urges that time and space be found to get things right' (Stirling, 2013). For the social theorist Bruno Latour, the precautionary principle, understood more broadly, calls for 'experimentation, invention, exploration, and of course risk-taking... For all our actions we consider risk-taking and precaution-taking as *synonymous*: the more risk we take, the more careful we are ... care and caution go together with risk-taking' (Latour, 2011). A precautionary approach suggests therefore an experimental and transformative attitude to history, one which involves being mindful of the risks we are taking now, in taking care of the future. Perhaps then, we need *pre-cautionary tales*.

Pre-cautionary tales invite us not to worry so much about foresight or prognostics — there is no telling what the future holds or where it all ends. Instead, these tales might work with an imagination of the future based on the ethics of care rather than solely on the technical management of the predicted risks and hazards associated with climate change. In a situation where all our predictions and predictive models are likely to fail, we should make more time to develop our capacity for storytelling as a means of weighing up the risks — of recalibrating and revising our collective actions in the present. Through telling stories to each other, we might practice becoming more adept at navigating situations that are dynamic, shifting and contingent, whether catastrophic or more gradual. Stories rely on our locatedness and groundedness — in other words on our humility — but also on an open-ended questioning of our place in time. Rather than think of our current predicament as one which necessitates a series of constraints that hedge against an inevitable planetary catastrophe, it might be important to reflect on a more provisional engagement with the world we are living in now. Uncontrollable calamities as well as the unintended consequences of our actions will always threaten the fragile order we create. A fast-changing climate doesn't allow for stable conditions. We may therefore also need to acknowledge that many of the adaptive strategies for our present-day cities and infrastructures are experiments which are necessarily precarious. We are, as ever, on unsure ground here.

When it comes to cautionary tales of the sky-falling and world-ending variety they invite us perhaps to think less about impending catastrophe and more about our capacity for world-changing — in all its possible manifestations, good and bad. In a fearsome and wonderful world full of surprises, humans can be surprising too.

Our present turbulent planetary moment (call it the Anthropocene if you like) requires working through the range of responses, resiliences and resourcefulness appropriate for human futures that are unknown and unpredictable and by turns scary and astonishing. It also suggests a following through with our responsibilities and continuing to care for unwanted consequences — however things turn out. The constant unravelling of the fragile urban fabric, its frequent reassembly and its inherent need for continued repair and maintenance relies on the accumulation of both experience and strategic thinking. The telling, listening to and re-telling of stories about climate change will continue to be run through with anxieties about our lack of foresight or our constant battling with the elements. However, in an uncertain world it is not necessarily important to know how it all ends; the story is really about the 'getting there', however messy, halting, incremental, sideways and unfinishable the journey. What matters is how we respond to what the world throws at us and what enabling stories, cautionary tales included, we continue to tell.

Let this be a warning then...

Words after things: narrating the ends of worlds

Bradon Smith

In his travel memoir *A Time of Gifts* (1977), the writer Patrick Leigh Fermor recounts his trip on foot through Europe in 1933-4. Written some 40 years later, it is infused with the knowledge of the war to come: of an end of the old European powers, and of the impending destruction that Europe would suffer in the coming years. It is, we could say, a pre-apocalyptic narrative.

In Persenbeug in Austria, Fermor meets a polymath in an inn on the banks of the Danube. Their conversation begins with the river and its fish species, but moves into a discussion of aristocratic titles. The man is upset by a sense of loss. He sees the extent of Germanic aristocratic titles as comic ('all handle but no jug!'), but cannot condone their being 'done away with'. He makes the comparison with extinct species: 'They should be preserved at all costs [...] history and ecology are against them. Think of the Oryx! Think of the Auckland Island Merganser! The Great Auk!' This leads him naturally back to the fish: 'Everything is going to vanish! They talk of building power dams across the Danube [...] All those fish from the East, they'll never come back! Never, never, never!' Leaving, the man stops to look at an 'enormous stuffed trout [...] swimming urgently through a tangle of tin weed' — a fish preserved at all costs — and, whistling Schubert's 'The Trout', then indicates to Fermor the window of a room in a castle on the hill, where Karl, the last Emperor of Austria, was born. For the man, these forms of loss — cultural, ecological, linguistic — are all interrelated; and just as the aristocratic titles have outlasted their meaningful use, so have the names of extinct species outlasted the creatures themselves.

Cormac McCarthy's *The Road* (2006), already becoming a classic of post-apocalyptic fiction, narrates a journey on foot of a very different kind, but the same idea of loss reflected in language — of 'the names of things slowly following those things into oblivion' — is important in the novel. *The Road* and the other two novels to be examined here have found in these interrelated forms of loss a way of engaging with the impact that we are having on the planet. In confronting a subject that has sometimes seemed too big and too slow to provoke great narratives, they have seen that what is affecting about climate change is the loss of loved ones, or the loss of species and biodiversity, or the loss of human culture itself.

In *The Road* a father and son (neither are named) walk south through a blasted landscape of burned trees and ash, battling the cold, interminable drizzle, constant hunger, and the threat of cannibalistic gangs. The novel makes no reference to climate change; indeed the 'event' that seems to have caused the destruction, vaguely described as 'a long sheer of light and a series of low concussions', would seem rather to conjure the fears of nuclear accident or attack that fuelled apocalyptic novels during the Cold War. Despite this, *The Road* has been repeatedly discussed as a climate change novel — George Monbiot going so far as to describe it as 'the most important environmental book ever written' (*The Guardian*, Oct 30, 2007).

Loss is everywhere in *The Road*. But it is the denuded landscape that leaves the deepest impression: ash, grey cloud, rain, the blacktop. As realised in John Hillcoat's film adaptation (2009), this is a landscape stripped of colour. This is partly because *The Road* is an interesting inversion of the popular post-human visions in which houses crumble, but trees and plants remain and, indeed, reclaim. In J.G. Ballard's novel *The Drowned World* (1962) the flora and fauna have reached colossal sizes in the dramatically warmed world, and even temperate London has become so hot as to be uninhabitable, as the earth regresses to earlier climatic conditions. In Ballard's novel the colours of the sun and of the jungle are oppressive. Alan Weisman's bestselling non-fiction book *The World Without Us* (2007) attempts to predict the gradual deterioration and destruction of buildings and artefacts in a world without humans, and nature's reclamation of even urban environments. In 500 years, he estimates, little would be left of a typical house save stainless steel saucepans and plastic handles. This same image, of houses and cities succumbing to vegetation, is a common visual trope in futuristic landscapes from films like *I Am Legend* (2007) — the most recent adaptation of Richard Matheson's novel — to recent post-apocalyptic TV series like *Revolution* (2012), and narrative video games like *The Last of Us* (2013). Asked in an interview about the landscapes for *The Last of Us*, developer Neil Druckmann (who elsewhere acknowledges the influence of *The Road*) replied that 'It's very much a destroyed landscape, but one that is also very, very beautiful as the lush plant life of nature has taken over.'

There is little of that beauty in McCarthy's vision: the trees are blackened stumps, but the houses stay standing. When the father and the boy see a lake with its hydroelectric dam, this inversion is brought to the fore. The father has to explain the purpose of the dam, because for the boy electricity is just another feature of the lost world that he has learned about. The boy asks:

> Will the dam be there for a long time?
> I think so. It's made out of concrete. It will probably be there for hundreds of years. Thousands, even.
> Do you think there could be fish in the lake?
> No. There's nothing in the lake.

The concrete dam remains; organic life is gone. McCarthy's is in some ways the more shocking vision — one that confronts us, as the novel does across many levels, with our attempts to cope with loss. There is a sanitisation to *The World*

Without Us: Wiesman has said that he removed humanity from the picture partly because it makes this problematic subject more bearable; in short, no one is left to grieve. By contrast, the special tragedy of *The Road* — as the mother, who chooses suicide, realises — is of those who must endure the loss of the world.

The loss of things and the loss of words

But perhaps *The Road*'s keenest examination of loss is manifested in the language of the novel. The dialogue and narration are generally sparse and repetitive, as monotonous as the landscape: 'after a while the boy stopped shaking and after a while he slept [...] He slept and woke and the rain slackened and after a while it stopped [...] He raised up from time to time to look to the east and after a while it was day.' Sometimes the dialogue seems to consist entirely of the word 'okay'. Language and loss: McCarthy underscores the connection throughout. How can the son understand the phrase 'as the crow flies', when crows only exist 'in books'? In a world in which there are only degrees of cold, and in which survival is day-to-day, what could phrases such as 'warm at last' and 'long term goals' really mean? 'The last instance of a thing', McCarthy tells us, 'takes the class with it'; and though language may last a little longer, it is brief respite: 'The names of things slowly following those things into oblivion. Colors. The names of birds. Things to eat. Finally the names of things one believed to be true. More fragile than he would have thought.' In some ways, this is a novel about the death of language, one that is narrating the destruction not only of the world, but also of the material from which it is itself formed.

So it is paradoxical that this is a novel that whilst spare in form, and set in a world devoid of colour, is occasionally rich in its vocabulary: 'gambreled', 'vermiculate', 'loess', 'torsional', 'salitter', 'rachitic'. McCarthy is keenly aware of this paradox of language: that it can exist where nothing else can. Words come adrift from the moorings of their signification, the signifier following the signified 'into oblivion'; and in McCarthy's altered world, created in words, words themselves are sometimes inadequate. Hearing a 'distant low rumble' the father thinks it, 'A sound without cognate and so without description.' This imponderable leads the man on to questions — 'what will you say? A living man spoke these lines? He sharpened a quill with his small penknife to scribe these things in sloe or lampblack?' How, the father wonders, and McCarthy asks, will we narrate the end of the world?

Michael Chabon has wondered the same thing. In his 2007 review of *The Road* in *The New York Review of Books* he identifies the paradox that 'to annihilate the world in prose one must simultaneously write it into being' — in the destruction that the novel conjures up is contained the creativity of that act of conjuring. But McCarthy would seem to be already acutely aware of this double-bind: the father, like McCarthy, is a teller of stories, and faces the same paradox, in inverted form. Whilst McCarthy cannot describe the world's destruction without writing the world into existence, the father 'could not construct for the child's pleasure the world he'd lost without constructing the loss as well'. The result is the nihilistic conclusion that in this world, there is no redemption to be found in imagination, or in storytelling.

Second chances

Jeanette Winterson's novel *The Stone Gods* is not nearly so bleak as *The Road*, and is poignant and sentimental in a way that *The Road* is not, but it too presents us with visions of loss. The novel is formed of four chapters or connected stories, with environmental destruction an important theme in each chapter.

The first is set on the planet Orbus, which the human inhabitants have so polluted as to make it uninhabitable. They have identified a new planet, Planet Blue, on which they plan to settle — once they have killed the dinosaurs that live there by diverting an asteroid into the planet to produce a short-lived dust cloud. They miscalculate, creating a mini ice age; stranded, a small group attempt to survive and settle there. The second chapter tells the story of the deforestation of Easter Island from the perspective of a shipwrecked English sailor. The third and fourth chapters, seemingly set on Earth (formerly Planet Blue) in the near future, narrate a backstory of climate change, the '3 War' and the gradual global control of the corporation 'MORE'. Different incarnations of the same two central characters recur across these three narratives: Billie Crusoe — a woman in the party sent to colonize Planet Blue; also the shipwrecked sailor — and Spike or Spikkers — a highly intelligent 'robo sapiens'; also a marooned Dutch man living on Easter Island.

Thematically, *The Stone Gods* is about second chances, and our failure to take them; like *The Road*, it is also about loss. These themes are mirrored in, on the one hand, our destruction of nature and on the other, in love and grief. The first chapter describes the society in which Billie Crusoe lives, and against which she quietly rebels: a society that 'clones its meat in labs and engineers its crops underground [and] thinks natural food is dirty and diseased'; and in which everyone is 'fixed' at the age they prefer (women cater for men's desire for younger and younger women); and a planet that is 'evolving in a way that is hostile to human life'. Or as Billie puts it, we 'fucked it to death and kicked it when it couldn't get up'. For a hundred years 'the doomsters and the environmentalists kept telling us we were as good as dead' but then, 'hey presto, not only do we find a new planet, but it is perfect for life. This time, we'll be more careful. This time we will learn from our mistakes.' A second chance.

The Stone Gods draws parallels between personal love and love and care for the planet, and between the grief for the loss of a loved one and the forms of loss threatened by environmental disaster. Where in *The Road*, the boy is literally everything for the father — they are 'each the other's world entire' — so *The Stone Gods* creates a series of similar relationships, extending this analogy between our love for someone, and our love of the world.

Billie is sent on the mission to colonise the new planet along with the privateer Captain Handsome, the vacuous competition winner Pink McMurphy and the beautiful cutting-edge of humanoid robotics, the *robo sapiens* named

Spike. Talking about the polluted planet Orbus, Pink denies responsibility: 'Don't blame me [...] I didn't destroy it'; Spike replies, 'But you have a second chance. Maybe this time...' and Pink makes the connection to personal relationships, singing 'Maybe this time, I'll be lucky, Maybe this time he'll stay...'

As Spike and Billie begin a love affair that challenges Billie's idea of the boundary between human and non-human, they too realise that they have become the entire world for the other: Spike comes to understand that love poetry is inspired by the idea that 'the stretch of the body-beloved is the landmass of the world', and the line from Donne's 'The Sun Rising' — 'She's all states, and all princes, I' — acts as a recurrent declaration of love. Donne's image of the world 'contracted thus' to the lovers' bed is mimicked in both the first and second chapters, as first Billie and the *robo sapiens* Spike and then Billie and Spikkers reduce the whole world to the caves where they will love, and then will die. In the second chapter, Billie's love for Spikkers has made his shipwreck on Easter Island into a life — 'I have shrunk this pod of an island further and made our cave an everywhere.' In these repeated connections between the loved one, and the whole world, lies the possibility of redemption: in the end, the novel seems to say, we may be capable of the empathy needed for a more sustainable way of living.

AD: After Dave, après le déluge

In *The Road* and *The Stone Gods*, McCarthy and Winterson create future dystopic societies, but within which love remains possible; both establish analogies between loss on a personal level and loss of habitats, species and 'nature' on a planetary environmental level. In his novel *The Book of Dave*, Will Self takes this further: the relationship is not analogous, but somehow causal. The plot of the whole novel is hinged absurdly but wonderfully on the idea that the dystopia of a future society 500 years hence is literally the result of the loss of his son suffered by an embittered London cabbie, Dave, in our own present.

Denied access to his son by a court restraining order, Dave has a schizoid episode and writes a book containing all his views on the world and society — his legacy for his 'Lost Boy' — and buries it: 'a bundle of proscriptions and injunctions [...] derived from the working life of London cabbies, a cock-eyed grasp on a mélange of fundamentalism [and his own] vindictive misogynism', as his psychiatric doctor describes it. Hundreds of years later, rising seas caused by climate change have turned hills into islands, and left England as an archipelago; and the 'Book of Dave' is the foundational text of a new society and its religion.

In hints that look forward from our present, and half-remembered history from 500 years AD (After Dave) we can piece together the effects of climate change on England. In 2002, Dave intuits the coming flood, which is prefigured in a number of episodes. In a dream, Dave feels 'an aqueous queasiness when he saw the long line of the North Downs to the far south — they were distant islands, uninhabited and uninhabitable. At his back he sensed the ridge of Barnet and then the Chilterns rising up, wooded shores against which London lapped'; a few months later Dave picks up a fare, a runner on a 'sortuva awfurred film about the Thames. This guy, see, he thinks the river's gonna flood and all the like... well, like shit an' that, is gonna come y'know... bubbling up to the surface'; and hearing for the first time about his Book, the doctor who eventually takes an interest in Dave finds himself watching the gulls 'riding the thermals over Whitestone Pond. *What is it with these seafowl?* he wondered. *Have they come inland because they anticipate a deluge? Should we get maintenance to start building an ark?'*

In a chapter set in 2003, we see an indication of the climate change to come: an unnaturally warm autumn is followed by only a brief winter: 'Winter was a long time in arriving that year. The earth refused to relinquish its heat, no winds came and the leaves, declining to exit the trees, remained there limp and furled.' When the winter does come, it lasts only two pages and then spring returns: 'the daffodils stalked from the copses in January — the apple blossom burst before the end of February. Winter, outgunned, retreated.'

In one of the novel's numerous echoes between our near past and distant future, the autumn of 522 AD is likewise late, causing disquiet and evoking memories of the past changes in the climate. The rain, called 'screenwash' by England's inhabitants of the future,

> came late that autumn — not until NOV was almost over [...] this year it seemed as if kipper [winter] would never arrive [...] The community became uneasy. The oldest of the grannies and grandads told tales of former times, when during such spells freakish waves had reared up out of the Great Lagoon, drenching the home field with curry [salt] and destroying the soil's fertility for a generation.

Partly facilitated by the split narrative between the late twentieth century and the sixth century After Dave, the novel shows us the changes in landscape, climate and society, but as the chapters set in our near past progress we also see the changes that come over Dave himself. In 1987, Dave 'loved everything to do with driving — driving made him feel free. It was easy, it was simple, it was open to all. The minute you got in a vehicle and turned the ignition the world was revved up with possibilities.' It is this freedom that leads him to life as a cabbie. But from freedom the cab becomes a form of imprisonment, and by 2003 Dave sells it, and walks out of London, sloughing off the city and his former life: 'He was losing it — whole chunks of the city were falling out of him'. Gradually the city gives way to 'saw-leafed patches of nettles and the whippy stalks of brambles'. He feels the city emptying out of him: 'He was disembowelled — he was losing it; and as he lost it the crushed plastic bottle of his soul expanded with sudden cracks and pops.'

As Dave leaves the city on foot — the novel's crux — he foresees the deluge:

> The city was a nameless conurbation, its street and shop signs, its plaques and placards, plucked then torn away by a tsunami of meltwater that dashed

up the estuary. He saw this as clearly as he'd ever seen anything in his life [...] he was privileged with a second sight into deep time. The great wave came on, thrusting before it a scurf of beakers, stirrers, spigots, tubes, toy soldiers [...] and a myriad other bits of moulded plastic, which minutes later washed up against the hills of Hampstead, Highgate, Harrow and Epping, forming salt-bleached reefs, which would remain there for centuries.

Then, symbolically, Dave 'turned and wandered away into the woodland.'

Animals out of time...

In the introduction to his *Book of Barely Imagined Beings*, Caspar Henderson (who also contributes to this volume) explains the connection between his deep sense of our responsibility for the planet, and the book's concentration on some of the world's more wonderful animal inhabitants. Noting the ubiquity of animals in prehistoric cave-paintings, he stresses the care and knowledge involved in those representations: 'All this', he realises, 'points to something obvious but which is, I think, so important that it is hard to overstate. And that is that for much of human history attempts to understand and define ourselves have been closely linked to how we see and represent other animals.' As he goes on to describe, the mode of this representation may change, but the 'other ways of being' that we confront when we look at animals ask important questions about who we are, and how we 'are' in the world.

'Climate change novels' take their place in this line of forms of representation. They often place the forms of loss that threaten our planet in parallel with loss on a personal level — that of a child, or a loved one. But all these novels also identify an important analogy for natural destruction in the loss of particular animals and species, which stand in for a loss of biodiversity on a much larger scale, but perhaps also for the loss of our own wonder at nature. These representations are, one suspects, as much about us, and how we are in the world, as they are about those non-human ways of being.

In some climate change novels, animals are at the heart of the narrative. In Barbara Kingsolver's recent novel, *Flight Behaviour*, Monarch butterflies are central to the story, to the novel's themes, and to its engagement with climate change. Forced by the changing climate to abandon their customary roosting grounds in Mexico, the butterflies attempt to overwinter in the small Appalachian town of Cleary instead, shaking up the life of a young woman, Dellarobia Turnbow, and bringing Ovid Byron, the lepidopterist, to the town.

In *Flight Behaviour*, the butterflies represent a loss equivalent to those of a child or a loved one: Ovid Byron literally grieves for them. Dellarobia notices his changed mood, but it is only when he tells her of the possibility of their extinction, that she sees that 'this was the bad news he'd received over the holiday. The one thing most beloved to him was dying. Not a death in the family, then, but maybe as serious as that. [...] Now began the steps of grief.' But the Monarchs also represent hope and freedom. Through helping Ovid with his work with the butterflies, Dellarobia gains the confidence and belief to finally escape her constraining life.

In *The Road*, the absence of animal life is an essential part of the bleak grey of the landscape; but typically, the animals' absence from the landscape is countered by the frequency with which they enter the language of the novel. The father's dreams are full of lost animals and 'so rich in colour'. Following immediately on from seeing the dead, dammed lake referred to earlier, the father remembers that 'in that long ago [...] he'd watched a falcon fall down the long blue wall of the mountain and break with the keel of its breastbone the midmost from a flight of cranes.' Elsewhere, the father remembers 'once in the early years' hearing 'flocks of migratory birds' and even though he thinks they fly 'as senselessly as insects trooping the rim of a bowl', still their flight feels like a departure: 'He wished them godspeed until they were gone. He never heard them again.' At another moment, he smells 'the lingering odour of cow [...] and realized they were extinct.'

The novel's final cryptic paragraph — a memory (whose?), an imagining, or perhaps a eulogy — is one example of the novel's occasionally lush vocabulary:

> Once there were brook trout in the streams in the mountains. You could see them standing in the amber current where the white edges of their fins wimpled softly in the flow. They smelled of moss in your hand. Polished and muscular and torsional. On their backs were vermiculate patterns that were maps of the world in its becoming. Maps and mazes. Of a thing which could not be put back. Not be made right again. In the deep glen where they lived all things were older than man and they hummed of mystery.

Here, the precision of McCarthy's vocabulary comes into its full force: 'wimpled' perfectly describes the veil-like movement of the fins (OED, v. 4. To fall in folds), but also has a cognate associated with streams (OED, v II 6. Of a stream: To meander, twist and turn; also, to ripple); 'vermiculate' gives us not only the contours of both trout and maps as 'ornamented with sinuous or wavy lines or markings of a specified colour' (vermiculated, adj. 3.) but also suggests the deep time of the fish's worm-like ancestors (vermiculated, adj. 1a [...] covered or ornamented with markings resembling those made by the gnawing of worms); 'amber' precisely conjures the peaty hue of a trout tarn, but also somehow fossilises and preserves this fish through the ages.

The brook trout represents the colours and forms that have been lost; but coming at the end of the novel, with the narrative hinting at a future for the boy as he finds a new family, this passage seems to exist outside time. With the father dead, we wonder who is remembering this trout, and this place where 'all things were older than man'. The freedom that the fish represents — like the Danubian fish described by Fermor's polymath, crossing continents unimpeded — includes a sense of timelessness.

In *The Book of Dave*, during his epiphany as he walks out of London, Dave crosses the M11, and sees the 'drivers' faces [...] jaws bunched, eyes white-rimmed with exhaustion.' The ex-cabbie realises that 'they would always be pinioned in this moment, while he was free to swim in the entire current of fluvial time.' Like McCarthy's vermiculate trout, like the fish in the Danube, Dave is no longer a trapped Driver, but rather, in this moment of his return to nature, swims 'outside time'.

This timelessness is also to be found in *The Stone Gods*. Stuck in a 'hi-tech, hi-stress, hi-mess' futuristic society, part of Billie's rebellion is to live anachronistically on a farm: 'Twenty hectares of pastureland and arable, with a stream running through the middle like a memory. Step into that water and you remember everything, and what you don't remember you invent.' Here, as in McCarthy, the stream again evokes deep time. In a lyrical reverie, Winterson suggests the interdependence of life in nature:

> The soil is deep clay and the cattle makes holes in it where they herd to feed. The holes fill with water, then ice over, and the birds crack open the ice to drink. The woodland belts that hold the fields are thick with branches thick with birds [...] the tiny blue violets that grow where the cattle go [...] The trout shy in the reeds. The carp dozing on the riverbed.

The passage is as syntactically interwoven as the web of life it describes: the repetition — 'cattle ... holes ... holes ... ice ... birds ... ice ... thick with branches thick with birds ... cattle' — ties each new organism to the others. The 'deep clay' reinforces the depth of time; the woodlands don't surround the fields, but 'hold' them; and every organism has its habitat — the trout in the reeds, the carp on the riverbed.

Final thoughts, last lines
It is a perennial question in the arena of arts and literature that engage with climate change to wonder what effect such creative work can have. Thought about narrowly, in terms of immediate and effective behaviour change, this will likely only ever give a disappointing answer. But looked at together, the more successful climate change novels do partly answer, I think, Caspar Henderson's call for careful consideration of how we understand our place in the world. It is literature's ability to present the world to us as we haven't seen it before that allows it to make a contribution to this debate.

While scientific, technocratic and media attention has focused on scientific disputes, or on technological or policy 'solutions' to the 'problem' of climate change, the novels discussed here have taken on the more difficult question: what exactly is it that is 'bad' about climate change? Finding an answer in the many interconnected forms of loss that it will bring about — of loved ones and family, of other species, of beauty, of humanity, of culture — they also suggest part of our capacity to respond. In our love for these things, and in our grief for their passing, they suggest that we may have the empathy for others, human and non-human, that we will need to live more lightly on the earth.

In *The Road*, *The Stone Gods* and *The Book of Dave*, the possibility of redemption is present in the analogous possibility of personal love. McCarthy's 'father' knows that he can only live while he has the child to live for; Billie and Spike see that to love another is to love a whole world; and Dave's 'salvation' comes in the unlikely forms of Phyllis, the kindly woman who 'rescues' him, and who then encourages him to write a second book, a declaration of hope and a recantation of the previous tome.

Changed by his new-found experiences of the countryside outside London, Dave realises the bitterness of his previous views. In his second book he urges his son (and by implication us all) to:

> strive always for RESPONSIBILITY, to understand that WE MAKE OUR OWN CHOICES IN LIFE, and that BLAMING OTHERS is not an option [...] the ice caps may melt, the jungles shrivel, the prairies frazzle, the family of humankind may have, at best, three or four more generations [...] yet there can be no EXCUSE for not trying to DO YOUR BEST and live right. Put a BRICK IN THE CISTERN, clean the ugly smear of motor oil from beneath your TRAINERS and walk away from the city.

The cyclical plotting of *The Stone Gods* — the potential and actual, futures and pasts all merge — might seem to deny our ability to make changes in the way Dave advocates, and suggest our disempowerment: fated to continue a cycle of destruction, turning successive planets into Easter Islands. But this novel too is shot through with hope: in Billie's ability to overcome her prejudices about the distinction between robot and human life, and fall in love with the *robo sapiens* Spike, Winterson presents us with a striking example of our potential to empathise with and love life other than our own. As Spike and Billie discuss the definition of life in *The Stone Gods*, Spike reminds her, 'there are many kinds of life [...] Humans always assumed that theirs was the only kind that mattered. That's how you destroyed your planet.' All the novels discussed here suggest the possibility of it being otherwise — of caring for the human and non-human world alike.

The Stone Gods leaves space for our intervention: as much as it is about second chances, it is also about choices. When Billie complains that life 'doesn't make sense. We make plans. We try to control, but the whole of this is random', Spike tells her, 'this is a quantum universe [...] neither random nor determined. It is potential at every second. All you can do is intervene.' This idea returns in the final pages:

> a universe of potentialities, waiting for an intervention to affect the outcome. Love is an intervention.
> Why do we not choose it?

Love in this novel, we remember, is for the other who also represents the whole world. Billie, along with others who have already chosen to abandon (and have been abandoned by) the military corporate society, makes a choice — an intervention — to stand with a rebellion against the state and the MORE-Peace army: an attempt to 'wake people up to what's really going on and to change things'. During the protest she is shot, and in the novel's (and her own) final moments, it is the timeless farm (belonging to the Billie character from a different time) that she sees, crossing the ages:

> On my left is a broad, active stream with watercress growing in the fast part [...] and a foam of frogs spawn and a moorhen sailing the current.
> I know this track, this stream, I've been here before many times it seems, though I can't say when.

The novel's final line — 'Everything is imprinted for ever with what it once was' — is strikingly similar to McCarthy's trout imprinted with 'the maps of the world in its becoming'. Both remind us of the far-reaching consequences of actions — everything is left with the imprint of the past. In the maps and mazes on the brook trout are revealed two paths: one a way out of this mess, and one that takes us further in.

In conversation

'In Conversation' is a transcript of a panel discussion at the 'What Sort of Story is Climate Change?' event organised by the Mediating Change Group and Free Word on 3 December 2013. Taking part were: Caspar Henderson, author of *The Book of Barely Imagined Beings*; Zoë Svendsen, theatre-maker, METIS performing arts company, and Lecturer in Drama and Performance, University of Cambridge; Nick Drake, poet and author of *High Arctic*; and Kate Fletcher, Reader in Fashion, London College of Fashion. It was chaired by Joe Smith, Senior Lecturer in Geography, the Open University. The audio recording was transcribed by Lauren Mooney. It has been lightly edited to reduce repetition and for clarity. A podcast is available at www.open.ac.uk/researchcentres/osrc/news/what-sort-of-story-is-climate-change?

Joe Smith: Welcome to 'What Sort of Story is Climate Change?', with four speakers from a range of disciplines, who have worked with this question in one way or another. I'm going to ask Caspar to lead us off with his responses to the question.

Caspar Henderson Much of my work over the last 21 years has related to climate change in one way or another, and during that time I have mainly lived with four stories.[1] The first I call *Pragmatist's Dream*. In this story, we live in a world where reasonable people of good will can work together to meet the challenges presented by climate change no matter how intractable and daunting they may seem. This story has a powerful driving force, and it informs much if not most of the progressive thinking and action in politics, business and society more generally.

I call the second story *Nothing Changes*. In this, the science of climate change is getting better all the time, the risks are, for the most part, becoming clearer, and the need for action more compelling, but the world is still heading, hell for leather, on a path of self-destruction. A glance at the trajectory of global emissions over the last 20 years and their likely future course seems to support this. But the story doesn't end there: we have to understand why nothing is changing. I remember going to a workshop organised by the group Platform [http://platformlondon.org], some time around the millennium, in which we were presented with a large number of charts and graphics relating to climate change over the previous 20 years and asked to identify a trend — apart, that is, from the steady rise in atmospheric concentrations of greenhouse gases. We puzzled for some time before the organisers pointed it out: the share prices of oil companies had risen steadily throughout the entire period. They were making a killing. And this is the second part of *Nothing Changes*: the bad guys are still there, and still in charge. Privately owned corporations — as well as those controlled by states in many parts of the world — will do almost anything to protect their profits from coal, oil and other enterprises that generate massive emissions. This kind of opposition cannot be moved by rational argument on the risks of climate change. We continue to live in societies dominated, in energy generation as much as in banking, by enterprises which will do almost anything to further their short-term profits.

The third story I will call *Angel Heart* after the 1987 movie starring Mickey Rourke and Robert DeNiro, in which (spoiler alert) when we finally meet the villain he is 'us'. In this story, it's not the corporations or the banks that are to blame (or at least not only them), but our civilisation or even our species as a whole. Something like this view (of industrial civilisation, though not necessarily humanity as a whole) informs the thinking — or perhaps the feeling more than thinking — of the Dark Mountain Project or someone like Roy Scranton, the author of a philosophical reflection titled 'Learning How to Die in the Anthropocene'. There have been times when I have found some variant of *Angel Heart* compelling, but in the end I usually find it the least convincing of the four stories I'm outlining here.

The last story, I call *Zhuangzi*, after the ancient Chinese sage who lived in about the 4th century BC. You've probably heard his tale of the philosopher waking from a dream in which he was a butterfly, and then wondering could he perhaps be a butterfly dreaming he is man? The point here is that Zhuangzi was a bit of an anarchist. He allowed for unusual possibilities, and I use his name for a story in which, despite all the grim signs, surprise and radical, disruptive change for the better is possible. There's a nice phrase from the economist and thinker Albert O. Hirschman. He talks of 'the discovery of paths, however narrow, leading to an outcome that appears to be foreclosed on the basis of probabilistic reasoning alone.' So even if things look really bad, they might not be as bad as you think, in spite of all the evidence. And those are the four stories.

Thank you. Tone is something that's very important in the decisions you made about your book [*The Book of Barely Imagined Beings*], and that will be obvious in the reading that you offer at the end — there's something about a fresh tone that invites more people in, and that makes sense of unusual possibilities that open up in addressing a topic. And unusual possibilities have been part of the work that you do, Zoë, around drama.

Zoë Svendsen I've got three stories! I'm a newcomer, I think, compared with many people in this room, to the problem of climate change. But I want to start in 2003 with a report entitled, 'An Abrupt Climate Change Scenario, and Its Implications for United States National Security'. My theatre company made a project called *3rd Ring Out* — we researched it from 2008 onwards, and we performed it in 2010 and 2011 — which was a staged rehearsal for a climate-changed future. And this document is something I came across as part of the research for that, so it's something I didn't know about in 2003 when it was written. The scenario started out with the idea that is now very familiar to us — that it's not about an incremental response to temperatures, where there'll be a measured response and adaptation to those rises, but that global warming entails extreme weather events that cause great disruption. This started out as a story, but has now become a kind of experience, so in the ten years, the position of this in relation to our sense of possibility has completely changed: it's no longer a worst case scenario, it's just life. The second point is, from 2008 I went from not knowing about climate change to knowing about it; that is, I did know about climate change, but I didn't *really* know about it. The project we were exploring was initially based around the Cold War, during which many people, about 17,000, would go down into bunkers all around the UK and spend a weekend or a couple of days pretending that nuclear war was happening. Now, as a theatre-maker I've never actually spent *that* long pretending something was happening, not in that intense way, and we were curious about what it meant to be someone who practised for disaster. So we were exploring all sorts of things, and the Cold War feels very old hat. We were interested in the form rather than the content, so our question was: what's the future threat that we might be facing, that we might need to practice for? That's when we started to think about climate change.

I went to the Climate Camp at Kingsnorth power station in 2008 to find out more about it. The story that I heard there was of the two degrees tipping point, and I was horrified at myself for not already knowing it — there was a sense in which myself, as a political being, was transformed by the fact that I thought I knew, and I clearly didn't. So there was a transformation that happened in that moment, that also transformed our project, which went from being a theatre piece in which we were investigating questions we were interested in, to some kind of mission, trying to normalise thinking about climate change in a framework that wasn't ordinarily used for that purpose — which was touring round theatre festivals. The idea of 'practising' being one that entails bringing in a capacity for thinking in everyday life about these questions. One of the things we looked at when we were doing the project was psychological thinking around traumatic limbo. Psychologists talk about this in terms of 'scriptlessness', the lack of an event schema. And emerging from this project, in a personal capacity, I feel that I don't have a script for action. So it's brilliant to be asked here tonight, because in a sense it feels like tonight is about trying to find scripts for action. But I also wondered whether my feeling about this is partly because I've slightly swallowed the story that it's down to me, and I feel isolated by that. I have a sort of active forgetting that circulates in my memory, which is that I feel I don't do anything, I'm not actively doing anything about this extraordinary, wide-ranging problem, and yet I kind of think about the fact that I'm not doing anything as I recycle the odd bottle, or whatever it is I *do* do. Actually, I feel it's not about any of us as individuals, and the script we need to look for is a larger social re-norming, that makes it easier for our short-term objectives to comply with the much longer-term objective of shifting a whole global way of doing things so that we can survive. So, that's my third story.

Thank you. Last year I went to the Ministry of Stories event 'The Story', and one of the people presenting was Fiona Romeo, the curator of the National Maritime Museum's Arctic show [*High Arctic*, 2011]. She talked about how they couldn't really bring [the exhibition] together, and someone came up with the bright idea of bringing Nick on board. The book of poetry he'll read from later and talk about now is the work that drew it all together. She said it gave meaning and a story to their work.

Nick Drake My story is one story and it's a beginner's story. I thought I would talk about that because it's the story of how I went to the Arctic with the arts/climate change organisation Cape Farewell, and then tried to write about that and about climate change. I was actually there — there's a picture of me on the cover, bestriding a pristine eco-system, probably doing it no good whatsoever. The trip was a wonderful experience. We sailed around the Svalbard Archipelago in a nineteenth-century metal-hulled ship. And it seemed to me that the Arctic was a dream-world, it amazed me, the enormous, ancient glaciers and fjords, but also the tiny and the transient, which was the glorious, miniature wonderland of the Arctic tundra in the summer. Light flew into the eye from every direction, reflected, amplified, refracted by water and sky and ice; silence ruled and time seemed to happen differently there. It seemed to me like a winter Eden, a place that changes you. But we were there not to think about ourselves so much as to be thinking about climate change: we had four scientists who patiently explained to us the melting ice cap, the warming ocean currents, human-made pollutants, biomagnification. Ice, it turned out, was one of the most valuable things on the planet. It keeps us as we are, in a relatively stable climate, and without it: *dot dot dot*.

So there we were, in a place of stunning beauty, but the lesson of it was that we were turning a winter Eden into a hell. I racked my brains about how I was going to respond to all this: what could a poem, what could words on a page actually do, or be, or mean in the face of something that seemed so daunting and huge? Who'd care? How could I do it without being preachy or didactic, propagandist or apocalyptic, or even just plain boring? And that's how it was for quite some time, until stories came along, to my rescue. I was commissioned by United Visual Artists to write a sequence of poems for their *High Arctic* exhibition at the National Maritime Museum [published as *The Farewell Glacier*, 2012], and I realised one way to confront the scale and complexity of the subject was to use voices, to tell the human story of the European relationship with the Arctic. There are obviously many Arctics, most importantly the indigenous Arctics, but I didn't feel I had any right to write about that. And as you walked through United Visual Artists' beautiful abstract installation, these ghosts would whisper their stories to you and you would listen. The subject seemed to fall naturally into three acts of the past, the present and the future. The past gave voice to explorers, mostly: from Pytheas the Greek, to Wally Herbert, who was the last great Arctic explorer, and also to the unnamed and unknown lost sailors, whalers and adventurers of three centuries. And the Arctic, it seemed to me, held up a mirror to all of them, revealing aspects of their humanity as they discovered it to be in such an inhuman place. I don't mean inhuman in a denigratory sense, it's just that it's not humanised land, and that's why it's wonderful and so important.

Wonder and terror seemed to be two sides of the same coin, and a theme seemed to emerge which was that human exploration and exploitation have long gone hand in hand. So curiosity, delight, wonder and terror have co-existed with greed, destruction and disaster — which says something about us, I think, both pessimistic and optimistic, as a culture and a species. The most exciting moment creatively came when I realised that parts of the non-human world could also talk back from their perspectives: I could find voices for creatures and elements as well as people; they also have stories, they have life stories, they have stories of love and survival and tragedy. So I tried writing soliloquies for the life and death cycle, stories of things like mercury and methane and tetrapods, which are these tiny little creatures at the base of the food chain. I never thought I'd write a poem about a tetrapod in my life, but strangely I did — and a poem in the voice of an ice core sample! The underlying theme of that section seemed to me something about awareness, certainly for myself: awareness of what we've done and awareness that we are the people who've changed nature, which is a phrase that, I gather, the Inuit say about us.

The section about the future was the most challenging to write because even now as the ice melts, energy companies, driven by their asset-stripping mentality and the insanity of quarterly returns are sizing up, vulture-style, the prospect of an ice-free Arctic. I felt obliged to tell what I saw as the true story about the tragic scale of climate change up there, and where it will almost now certainly end for the polar ice cap. In fact because of my love for the winter Eden of the Arctic, I felt obliged to lament its passing; and love and loss are really at the heart of all poetry.

At the same time I desperately wanted to find reasons to be cheerful, and a tone that wasn't all 'we're going to hell in a handcart', but was more confronting: What are we going to do? How are we going to do it? With 'we' being the emphasis. The storytelling aspect of the installation seemed essential to its relationship with the audience. They liked the stories, they connected with the history of climate change through the various voices, which had stories to tell them and things that needed to be said. But I feel I've only just begun to explore the possibilities of story for the big theme of climate change. Most of us feel a huge sense of powerlessness, of stuckness: we're up against such big odds, such short-term, short-sighted power; we're also, in a profound sense, up against ourselves. So one thing I'd like to explore more is, how do things change? How does change happen? Another is to write stories asking: Where do things we take for granted, such as energy and phones and clothes, come from? What does it take to make them? And to track this back to the beginning, so that they also tell their own stories. The other idea I'm playing with at the moment is that art needs to return to survival as a great and ancient theme. I feel our future survival must be an act of shared, multiple and communal imagination, and I'd like to tell stories that return a sense of power to the individual and the group. For not only are we in the hands of the future, but the future is in our hands too.

Kate, how does the story of climate change make an appearance in fashion?

Kate Fletcher In a way I'm representing — well, I suppose it's a cipher of consumerism, the fashion sector, and what I'm going to talk about are stories about climate change that have dominated fashion. It's a funny place to do work about sustainability. It's an odd place, where you get pulled in different directions — but perhaps the tension within it makes it one of the most vibrant places to be working in this area. In the past, stories about climate change, such as they are, have been shaped by a sense that issues in fashion rise and fall within supply chains. It's about fibre, fabric and garment production, and it's very rarely about demand, it's very rarely about consumers; it's very much about pointing the finger at 'them', the industry, and absolving people generally of blame. It tends to be industrial, the stories about climate change — very rarely individual or domestic. It's concentrated on mills and it's not really about social norms, it's not about the effects that are dispersed through homes and wardrobes.

In 2010 there were massive floods and huge droughts, and lots of cotton-producing regions were affected by these really substantial changes in weather conditions. And what happened is that the volume of production of cotton crop really dropped, as did its quality, and in that year alone the price of cotton almost doubled. This had massive developments — because not only did the price of cotton double, but the price of polyester also almost doubled; as everybody was trying to rush to supply fabrics of a cheaper quality, they moved to polyester instead. People started blending cotton and polyester together to try to keep prices low, and what you saw was this massive shift, this change that was passed on to consumers in a small way. Natural fibres like cotton and wool take lots and lots of water to get them to the market and very little energy, and fibres like polyester and nylon, the synthetic ones, take lots of energy and very little water. What we're faced with are massive fluctuations as natural conditions begin to change. So what's the industry done? It's made some great techno-fixes. There's a polyester fibre that you can get with 80% fewer greenhouse gas emissions. They're reducing humidity and changing heating efficiencies in factories. You also see labelling happening, with the Carbon Trust telling us that six and a half kilos of carbon are generated for every cotton T-shirt produced. Then you see some guys who are going off grid, and treadle sewing machines being used, making nice little natty dresses.

All of these responses are really happening. And what's this achieved? To be honest, not much. There's a tiny recalibration of the sense of what is involved in producing things within supply chains; maybe people see the true costs of things a little; maybe it underscores the view that the problem really is for the market to sort out, and it's all about engineering efficiency; but actually I think it just reinforces the view that most people have, that fashion equips us to appear in a world that has nothing to do with the earth. There's a massive disconnect between fashion and the earth, and all its conditions. But when I think about the sort of stories we can tell, it's a very different picture. These things have a tenor, a complexity, and also, dare I say, a modesty that industry initiatives don't have the heart and soul for. And it's about a broad spectrum of activity that no-one in industry really notices. So what I want to do is to show you the stories about climate change that I would like to tell. I've been talking to the public for about five years about how they use their things [as part of the Local Wisdom project]. What we find when we talk to people about the skills of 'usership', as distinct from ownership, is that they maintain things with great satisfaction and they express themselves, in a fashion context, in vibrant ways. What we see is a fabulous 'politics of less', we see a geography of hope, we see lots of very creative, very ingenious ways that people talk about an ethic of care. And it helps us see what clothes can mean outside a context of fashion production and consumption, particularly of new clothes. [Holds up photos. The images appear on the Local Wisdom website www.localwisdom.info] The guy on the left is wearing a housecoat, what I would call a dressing gown. They called them 'smoking jackets' back in the day. He layers up, he even puts a scarf on in order to keep the thermostat down! What we find the world over is people turning their thermostats down because bills are high and there's a sensibility about climate change. So people are starting to dress in the home like they used to. The woman in the middle is wearing a dress that is a multi-functional piece. She realised that it takes time to understand the potential of multi-functional garments like this one, and that fashion is obsessed with change and novelty, but in this case the slowness of it is something that really represents opportunities for doing things in a different way. People are often too obsessed with novelty being important to fashion, but actually fashion can be represented through stories of slowness, noticing and a patience that we've never given it credit for. The fashion industry is very good at valuing only a narrow spectrum of activity and saying it's important — but I think that what these things do, is point to a really broad spectrum of activity and say what fashion provision and fashion expression can be in a different sort of world. What we have at the end is a woman who's celebrating the use of safety pins, and showing what can happen when you build a self-reliance and an expression of fashion that's not just based on what the buyer in Selfridges thinks you should be wearing. When you take ownership over some of the difficult knowledge of what we must do, you see that people are two steps ahead of us sometimes — but it needs to be gathered and collected, and presented as a 'we', as a social norm. I think to work in an industry with such a dubious reputation and then to see things like this is actually a fabulous privilege, and a message of hope for us all.

Thanks, Kate. I'd now like to invite questions.

Daniel Nelson Can I ask about theatre? Of the theatre I've seen, there have been quite a few productions about climate change in the last eighteen months, and the only ones that have any sort of traction have been about climate change activists. I'm talking about an impact on audiences — because we've got to get through to people — and I wonder, is there a way out of this? It seems to be about activists because it's dramatic, they're fighting amongst themselves, it's fun, it is drama! But very little else has had an impact in the theatre.

Before we go to Zoë, I'd like to ask a couple of people in the audience to comment.

Bradon Smith One of the things I've noticed in theatre about climate change is attention to loss, particularly to familial loss, and the relationship between family and climate change. Often it's presented as a question about intergenerational justice, the relationship between parents and children. It's true that activism does come up a lot, but there are a lot of other interesting themes that sit slightly below the surface in theatre about climate change.

Charlie Kronick I work at Greenpeace UK and what activists do, or what they have been thought to do over time, is that we — 'experts' — explain things. First we stake out a kind of 'expert' status, identify a whole set of really important facts about everything from water use to energy use, and then explain to anybody who will listen, and a lot of people who don't listen, that as soon as they know what we know, they will start to behave differently.

Also, there's this huge emphasis on individual activity, that your responsibility is the thing that's making the planet worse or better, and I guess as somebody who's spent 20 years trying to change things, I notice the amazing, almost palpable failure of that model to do nearly anything. I think there's a hope that narrative can move you away from the facts that get in the way of acting, or feeling moved to act.

Alex Holland What drew me here tonight is that, to quote someone else, climate change is no longer a science issue, it's a sales issue — in terms of communicating it. I was really pleased by what Nick said, about trying to put the emphasis back on individual power and communal power, and the role of agency in it, because otherwise it can be this Cassandra-like doom, that we can all see it coming but not do anything to avoid it. How do we get there, what's the route? Futerra did a report called 'Sell the Sizzle' [www.futerra. co.uk], which gave justification for why this didn't work. It was based on a lot of good research involving DEFRA [the UK Government's Department for Environment, Food and Rural Affairs] and other people, which says that when you can't see a route to avoid doom it does become very disempowering, and what you should do is try and sell a positive image of the future, which people have a role in constructing. And then a way to get there. And then do the doom. But one of the big issues I've found is that in art, in stories, images of a happy future might excite you but they're often quite boring — there's a reason there's not a lot of utopian futures in fiction, that it's mainly dystopian, because apocalypse is a lot more exciting, right? But I'm hoping there is some scope for a Gene Roddenberry-esque story, a *Star Trek* for sustainability, where everything is great but there is still drama.

Star Trek **for sustainability, you heard it here first. I hope you've already registered the name. Among a slew of climate change-related plays I saw in London across a couple of years, the one I most enjoyed was Richard Bean's** *The Heretic* **(2011), which has a kind of 'the devil has all the best tunes' conclusion, intended to poke a finger in the eye of climate change orthodoxy. It also threw in plenty of gags, which seemed somehow significant.**

Robert Butler I wanted to pick up on the point about climate activists being at the centre of dramas, because obviously all drama needs great characters, and there's one character who has really been outstanding in this and has surfaced in a number of plays, or versions of him have surfaced, and that's James Lovelock [author of *Gaia, A New Look at Life on Earth*, 1979]. He combines two types that are very attractive in theatre: one is the Cassandra figure, who can see the future, and the other is someone who's slightly misanthropic and gleeful about what's happening. It makes him a very contradictory figure. And the best plays about science have these contradictory characters at their centre.

Zoë, do you want to respond?

Zoë Svendsen One of the things we found ourselves thinking about was the form of address in a theatre — that you have the audience on one side and the actors on another, and the topic does become about a group of people who have intrinsic relations to one another, activists or otherwise. That produces a kind of drama, seeking for a short-term set of consequences, which is difficult to achieve when you're talking about climate change, because the unknowns are much greater. That links into this issue about the script for action and the Cassandra problem. In the [Third Ring Out] project, we staged a climate crisis in which an audience sat in a cell that was built from a shipping container, and you had to vote about how to respond in a climate crisis.[2] But it wasn't an apocalypse, it was simply this set of interlinked problems that had emerged. The idea was to mimic those Cold War exercises by providing a kind of event schema for a climate crisis. So the emphasis was not on emotion, not on lament, and simply about acting and responding. But you were in a way the actor, and the action was, in a minimal, symbolic sense, the voting. Some schoolchildren came to see it, and one of them said, 'It's amazing, because they're always telling us to recycle, but they never tell us why!' There's a fear on the part of 'the people who know' of bombarding 'the people who don't know' because you say you want to have a happy future, but you also disenfranchise, by not acknowledging what we're facing. Because the other side of it is that all our actions matter more, they've never mattered more at any point in history than now. What we're doing suddenly has the grand scale of tragedy — if we're going to go back, right to the heart of drama, which is that the small things that we do are playing out on the most vast scale imaginable. And for the longest time we haven't had — we don't have any gods, we barely have kings — we haven't had the capacity for grand gestures. Hence there's another way of thinking about it which is perhaps more productive, but doesn't disallow the possibility that things could really be quite terrible.

Bridget McKenzie We talk a lot about stories in the cultural sector, but I want to push for us to create a more discursive cultural system, where stories are connected to other forms of cultural engagement. I see a kind of cycle, where stories are really quite central — and they should be stories of both grief and joy combined — and then connecting that to dialogue, which is then connected to deeper enquiry, which is then connected to designs for a better world, which are then communicated through stories, which are taken apart and re-designed, and so on. I don't want to take away stories from this discussion, but I'd like us to see it in a wider context.

Are there any particular examples that you feel, 'Yes, that's got it — that's, in a sense, what I'm talking about'? Does anyone else want to come in with that?

Lucy Neal I'm sure everybody's familiar with the work of Joanna Macy [environmental activist and scholar of Buddhism and systems theory], but I do find her framing of the three ways in which change is happening extraordinarily useful — because they allow for the simultaneous nature of the fact that everybody is doing everything and everything is actually possible, that change is happening. One way is activism — which is absolutely crucial because it identifies the causes, slows damage down, a sort of hospice worker for a system that's collapsing. The second is about alternative realities, structures, ways of organising — the green shoots. That's very energising to work with, because it's exploratory, it's creative, it is possible and positive. But the third way, which I think is so interesting for us to consider, is a sort of shift of values; this awareness both of the biological sciences, but also of our ancient tradition, and a greater, deeper sense that we are all connected. Those three systems work to create systemic change — whether they're stories or not — it's looking at the system of it that I find helpful.

Kate, can I consider that an invitation for you to talk a bit more about the interdependence, the interconnections that you've written and talked about, as in, for example, *Fashion and Sustainability: Design for Change* [co-authored with Lynda Grose; Laurence King, 2012]?

Kate Fletcher I spent some time on a boat in the Hebrides in the summer [as part of a cross-disciplinary expedition — www.whathastobedone.com], and I had an experience that really made me think differently about fashion and trying to think of fashion in a way that reflected the interdependency of our situation much more. It's very often seen as separate from the world, from landscape, from people's lives — and yet, while garments are really sold to us as products, we live them as a process. The moment they enter our lives, it's an ongoing, iterative process of change. The industry, of course, isn't set up to think about that, it doesn't want to think about that, and yet that's the reality. But when you speak to people about their engagement with stuff, it's only the industry that tells you it's all about churn and novelty; when you speak to people about how they use garments, quite a lot of people reflect these things you're talking about. I can identify quite a lot of folk that would build Joanna Macy's world in 3D and in garment form, and there's nothing more convincing than seeing somebody wearing a garment that is speaking to all these issues, and really reflects the interdependency of their lives with the places that they live.

That's an invitation, Nick, to talk about giving voice to 'things', in the way that you did in the High Arctic poems.

Nick Drake Yes. I want to say two things. When I came back from the Arctic, for about two weeks I felt completely alive with it, and I felt that I was going to change my life — because I'd seen what was there, I'd seen what we, in our world, had taken from that place. I'd seen the cost of it. I was going to change my life, and I was going to change the people around me; I was going to walk everywhere, I was going to recycle my clothes, all that kind of thing. That lasted about three weeks before I lost my first sense of power about it all. Given the enormity of the way we live now, I couldn't find a way to make what I'd learned work, but the connectivity of it had been incredibly important to me. The fact that I had seen that we are spending this treasury of ice in order to heat our homes suddenly became a real thing for me. And so I suppose, in my small way, what I was trying to do was to write some poems that reflected that sense of what the real connections between us and the world around us are, what the costs of those connections are and how we might think about those, so that when we have that understanding and that feel for it we might have a different response or a different attitude, or even a kind of responsibility for these things.

Caspar Henderson Can I pick up on something that Nick said? On celebration and paying attention — that's what I've tried to do in this book. We have experiences that, if we're lucky, if we're paying attention, teach us that life is amazing all the way down, right down to the atomic level, and it's quite precious and unlikely to be alive at any moment. I'd like to come back to the theme of tragedy at some point, too. I took part in a panel discussion about seven or eight years ago at the Bishopsgate Institute; I gave a talk on tragedy and climate change. Tragedy is a very powerful, formative influence in our culture, through the Greeks and through Shakespeare and other writers. People would say it's a form that a society that's very comfortable in itself can use, because sometimes it's so terrifying, and yet we do need to look — we need to look the Gorgon in the eye, as it were. Behind the Greek tragedies you've got, for example, among other things, Homer's *Odyssey* — which doesn't end in tragedy, though there are quite a few close shaves along the way... So I think we need to bring those very big, epic stories in and let them inform our thinking and our imagination.

Do any of you want to expand on that?

Zoë Svendsen Tragedy, for me, isn't about lament but about agency; for a tragedy to occur it requires an agent at the centre. By taking charge in that way, under difficult circumstances, it might offer something that isn't about impotence and sadness.

Caspar Henderson A Brechtian tragedy is about agency, but a Greek tragedy is about terrible forces which we can't control, irrational forces — inside people, but the world around us as well.

Zoë Svendsen Indeed, but it's structured by actions; so for instance, Oedipus caused his demise through his own actions, even though he didn't know. It still places human actions at the heart. Even though the characters' actions, in those instances, are to their detriment, they still stage processes of action, or a capacity for action, and I think we have a contemporary idea of an incapacity for action that's problematic.

Feimatta Conteh We [at the Arcola Theatre] just did a project that Nick was involved with, 'Climate Week Play in a Day', and we've just done a project with young writers writing about climate change. Small point about tragedy and climate change: I see what Zoë was saying, that Greek tragedy does sort of call for action, because you see the inhuman actors creating something and the impact of that on one human, the tragic hero, and what they do, and what would we do, and what do we learn from that? I think one of the main problems for me about the story of climate change is that the inhuman actors are so vague — it's capitalism — these aren't our gods any more but what's the human element in that? I know the people on the panel have mentioned, and I think it's really great, the isolating thing of 'me', and how do we make it a tragedy of 'we'? How do we act as a cohesive group in a tragedy?

Anna Jones [Like Charlie Kronick], I work at Greenpeace. One of the things I've been thinking about is that we may feel we're partly to blame for putting the onus on the individual, but actually at Greenpeace we spend a lot of time trying to think of ways to communicate that this isn't just about individual action, this is about governments and corporations. But sometimes I worry that we're creating new and other villains out of those entities, and there are people within them — obviously. Again, it's a narrative that works, the activist and the villain, you have characters people understand, but I'm interested in how we speak to the humans within those entities and create change from within. But I guess it's an open question about whether those kinds of clichéd ways of thinking about narrative, the hero and the villain, are useful, or whether we need to be thinking about other ways, where there's much more equality amongst the different actors — or much more subtlety, perhaps.

Charlie Kronick Whether you're talking about journalism or you're talking about drama or a novel, anything about climate change, the implication to me (and the thing that really frustrates me) is the idea that you need to get the whole thing organised in such a way that once you understand it, either emotionally or intellectually, you can then reconstruct it, pick it apart, and do the right thing and stop doing the wrong things. And it feels like if the world ever worked like that, then it definitely no longer works that way... It seems to me, anyway, that the biggest opportunities are not for transformation, although we want transformation, but for 'a poke in the eye', for disruption. Because without disruption, the big institutional relationships never shift.

Roger Harrabin I'm the BBC's Environment Analyst — I've been preoccupied with trying to communicate these issues for a very long time. The question 'Can journalism portray climate change better?' really begs another, which is, 'Is there one portrayal, is there one narrative of climate change?' Because, at the moment, you're seeing a very powerful counter-narrative running from the *Daily Mail* — which is campaigning against the 'great green con' — and the *Daily Telegraph*, and other journalists broadly from the right (although some from the left), who are campaigning very vigorously, suggesting that either climate change has been exaggerated or it hasn't been exaggerated, but the solutions proposed by governments, and by generally right-thinking people, the sort of people who I guess would think they were in this room, the suggestion now is that those solutions are wrong. So when you ask, 'is journalism making a bad job of communicating?', I would say the *Mail* and the *Telegraph* are making an extremely good job of communicating their case — and we can see the results of that communication in changing government policy. Now my guess is that people in this room would want another narrative, one which says climate change is serious and could be catastrophic for us if we're not lucky, and we're taking a big risk with the planet. The truth is, we have actually been saying that for the past 25 years. So our challenge as journalists is to find new narratives, new stories, new ways of telling stories. I'm constantly engaged in a search for them, but it gets more difficult as time goes on. Ideas gladly welcomed.

This question about what new narratives, what new stories, we might have available is absolutely essential to what we're trying to do with this and other work. I'm going to ask Caspar to read from his recently published book, *The Book of Barely Imagined Beings*, and we'll then move directly to Nick.

Caspar Henderson I'm going to read from the conclusion, and the title of the conclusion is 'A Conclusion in which Nothing is Concluded', which I stole from *Rasselas* by Samuel Johnson — very highly recommended, a kind of English version of Voltaire's *Candide*.[3]

> This book is an attempt to better understand and imagine being and beings. If I have made any progress at all, it will be thanks to what has been revealed by the vision and thought of others — especially what has been revealed by scientific method, which Richard Feynman defined as the best way we have learned about how to keep from fooling ourselves. But however powerful those insights and that method are, human understanding of the world that we are creating remains poor. In some respects, even the best maps and projections of our future are likely to prove little more accurate than a medieval *mappa mundi*.
>
> The last chapter cited a well-known line from *Candide*: 'we must cultivate our garden'. But what sort of garden are we cultivating in the

Anthropocene and what sort of creatures will flourish in it? How will things turn out? When will we know? A true gardener wants to be able to see into the future — a good 'eleven hundred years,' joked Karel Čapek 'to test, learn to know, and appreciate fully what is his'.

A few things look reasonably sure. Humanity will continue to have an enormous impact on the Earth system. The greenhouse gases we have added to the atmosphere will probably prevent any ice ages that would otherwise have happened for the next 48,000 years, and the way things are going it is likely we will prevent all those that would have occurred in the next half million years. In the nearer term, over the next century or two, we are in for a bumpy ride, unless we develop much better systems for managing resources and pollution and for anticipating and dealing with risks and conflict. Still, human creativity and innovation seem to be almost boundless.

When it comes to predicting how things will go with any precision, however, all these factors, and others, are like Rorschach's ink blots: we can read almost (but not quite) whatever we want into them. If the complexity of the Earth-human system means that much will remain necessarily unknowable, then we need, as two critics of transhumanism put it, to 'rehabilitate humility'. Only then can we listen to voices that are hard to hear, as well as those we want to hear. As in the story of Oedipus, the tragedy occurs when we refuse to listen.

Nick Drake The first part [of *Farewell Glacier*] I'm going to read is in the voice of the ice core — a first for all of us, I think! The idea is that ice, at least ancient ice, is like an enormous library of all the winters that have ever happened on the planet. Each winter is a page in a book in the library, and it contains the story of that year: it contains what was in the atmosphere, it contains secrets and wonders. It contains, for example, burning cities from Ancient Rome and so on; you can find remarkable things going back to the very beginning of time. And they are dug out of very ancient ice, these marvellous long cylinders. This is the ice core sample, telling — I think — her story.[4]

This is the library of ice,
A high security
Auditorium of silence
Far below zero;
An archive of cold
That keeps me as I am,
And reminds me of home
Now that it is gone
Forever.

I am a long story,
Ten thousand feet long,
A hundred thousand years old,
A chronicle of lost time,
Back to the first dark,
Too dark for telling;
I am every winter's fall;
I am the keeper of the air
Of all the vanished summers;
I honour the shadows of sorrows
That come to lie
Between my pages;
I distil lost atmospheres
Pressed into ghosts
Kept close to my cold heart.

And as for you —
What story would you like to hear?
On your two feet, tracking the snow
Two by two, two by two, two by two;
Here is the dust and music
Of your brief cities;
Here is the ash and smoke;
Here are your traffic jams
And vapour trails;
Here are your holidays in the sun
And your masterpieces
And your pop songs.
Here are your first cries
And last whispers;
Here are your long sighs
Of disappointment.
Here is where it went right,
And where it went wrong.
Easy come. Easy go.

So I know why you slice
Moon after moon from me,
Holding each fragile face
Up to your searchlights;
Why you measure and record
The tiny cracks and snaps
Of my mysteries;
Because you know

You are the people
Who have changed nature —
And now you are on your own.

I have no more to tell.
No questions please
About the future
For now the great narrator
Silence
Takes over;
Listen carefully to her story
For you are in it.

So she's quite pessimistic! As she would be, because her being is melting.
The other side of the coin is a poem spoken in the voice of the future. Again
I imagine her as a female, definitely.[5]

Dear mortals;
I know you are busy with your colourful lives;
You grow quickly bored,
And detest moralising;
I have no wish to waste the little time that remains
On arguments and heated debates;
I wish I could entertain you
With some magnificent propositions and glorious jokes;
But the best I can do is this:
I haven't happened yet; but I will.
I am the future, but before I appear
Close your eyes and listen carefully.
I can't pretend it's going to be
Business as usual.
Things are going to change.
I'm going to be unrecognisable.
Please, don't open your eyes, not yet.
I'm not trying to frighten you.
All I ask is that you think of me
Not as a wish or a nightmare, but as a story
You have to tell yourselves —
Not with an ending in which everyone lives
Happily ever after, or a B-movie apocalypse,
But maybe starting with the line
'To be continued...'
And see what happens next.
Remember this; I am not

Written in stone
But in time —
So please don't shrug and say
What can we do
It's too late, etc, etc, etc...
Already I hear the sound of empty seats
Clapping as you head for the exits.
I feel like the comedian who died.
Dear mortals,
You are such strange creatures
With your greed and your kindness,
And your hearts like broken toys;
You carry fear with you everywhere
Like a tiny god
In its box of shadows.
You love shopping and music,
Good food and festivals.
You lie to yourselves
Because you're afraid of the dark.
But the truth is this: you are in my hands
And I am in yours.
We are in this together,
Face to face and eye to eye;
We are made for each other.
Now those of you who are still here;
Open your eyes and tell me what you see.

1   Caspar's remarks drew on a longer essay he wrote for the
    Open University which can be found online at his website
    http://jebin08.blogspot.co.uk/p/blog-page.html The text that
    appears here has been modified to reflect some points in that essay.

2   See www.3rdringout.com; http://metisarts.co.uk/3rd-ring-out-the-
    research-context/.

3   Excerpt from: Caspar Henderson, *The Book of Barely Imagined Beings:*
    A 21st Century Bestiary, London: Granta Publications, 2012,
    pp. 377-378.

4   Excerpt from: Nick Drake, *The Farewell Glacier*, Northumberland:
    Bloodaxe Books, 2012, pp. 45-46.

5   Excerpt from: Nick Drake, *The Farewell Glacier*, Northumberland:
    Bloodaxe Books, 2012, pp. 49-50.

Eleven stories

One

Tan Copsey, Senior Communications Manager, Global Commission on the Economy and Climate

For hundreds of millions of people, climate change is embedded in their everyday lives. These people are probably not reading newspapers or arguing over science but they're noticing changes in the timing of seasons and in the crops they can grow. Over the past few years I've been working on Climate Asia — a study of people's perceptions of changes in climate and resource availability across seven Asian countries. Three-quarters of those surveyed said temperatures had risen. As one Bangladeshi government official put it, 'people may not know what climate change is, but they are feeling its impact'.

I hope to build on what we've found through Climate Asia to change the climate change story. There's a real need to communicate with more people, particularly those who already feel the impact. We need to get more people to share their stories about what they've done to respond to change, to inspire others to take action. The best person to communicate with a smallholder farmer in Nepal struggling with post-harvest loss is another farmer who is already doing something.

This isn't to say we shouldn't talk about reducing emissions or have scientific debates about extreme weather. But it's important to remember that when we read a story about global climate change negotiations illustrated with a picture of suffering people somewhere in Asia or Africa we're communicating *about* them rather than *with* them. This needs to change.

So how did I end up wondering and worrying about precipitation patterns in Vietnam and saline intrusion in Bangladesh? I grew up in New Zealand in the 1980s, a wild, green place at the end of the world. After the sinking of the Rainbow Warrior on our turf in 1985, ordinary people were broadly sympathetic to environmental causes and saw that it was possible to take action to deal with environmental issues. Unfortunately, I've always married this environmental interest with good old-fashioned British pessimism which kicks in during days spent trudging around international climate negotiations. Working on Climate Asia has made me optimistic about people's ability to adapt to changes in climate, but I'm still worried that we will create changes that many people can't adapt to. I'm now working with the Global Commission on the Economy and Climate to build better economies that create opportunities for all and that are resilient to coming changes.

Two

Kris De Meyer, neuroscientist

I study how our brains try to impose order and meaning on the sensory stimuli coming from the world around us. To me, therefore, the story of climate change is the story of how we are limited in our access to and grasp of 'reality'. Because our brains are preoccupied with 'social reality' (the 'others'), the story of climate change is also one of relationships gone wrong. Improve those relationships, and we can move forwards on the central problem too.

In the 13th century, Rumi, a Persian poet, wrote: 'The truth was a mirror in the hands of God. It fell, and broke into pieces. Everybody took a piece, they looked at it and thought they had the truth.' This proverb beautifully summarises the current standoff in the public debate about climate change. On all sides there are people who are convinced that they know what will happen, or convinced that they know what should be done — if anything. Within this plethora of beliefs about future and solutions, most of us, individually, will be proven wrong. Those of us who turn out to be right are mostly so by chance. Each week someone wins the lottery, while most of us get all the numbers wrong. I am not comparing science to a game of chance, nor do I advocate complacency. Rather, what I am saying is that if you are worried, keep this in mind: whatever future you see in your little shard, it hasn't happened yet.

Back to Rumi. There are those of us who think we have the truth. We celebrate our own rationality, our common sense. But can sense be 'common' if so many disagree? To avoid that question we invent stories to denigrate those on the other side: too stupid to see reality, too insane to reason with, driven by personal gain, or a desire to ruin the lives of others. If you find yourself thinking — 'But that is true!' — know that you can find the same stories on both sides of the divide.

In his recent book *The Social Animal*, David Brooks condenses 70 years of social attribution research into one beautiful line: 'We judge ourselves by our intentions, our friends by their behaviour, and our enemies by their mistakes'. What would happen if we stopped doing the latter? I do not think we'd start agreeing, but perhaps we could remember that, they too, picked up a single shard and thought they'd found the truth.

Three

Isabel Hilton, journalist

I am a journalist. Journalists tell stories. For several years now I have tried to understand, then to tell, the story of climate change in a way that makes it intelligible as both an existential threat to humanity and a fixable set of technical and scientific problems. It is proving curiously difficult, and not only because we try to do this for readers in Chinese and English, who may bring very different understanding to their reading.

There are many paradoxes in the climate change story: if the scale of the threat is not understood, there will be no chance of eliciting the political, economic and social responses it demands. But threats on this scale can paralyse as well as motivate: faced with an overwhelming task, we look for ways to avoid confronting it, and sceptics are always ready to offer diversions. To wait for proof definitive enough to silence the sceptics would diminish our room for intervention, eventually to the point of futility.

Journalists, traditionally constrained by the tight word limits of the now old-fashioned printed page and pressed for time, prefer clear, linear narratives with a beginning, a middle and an end: what happened? Why did it happen? Who is to blame? These narratives serve as a defence against the chaos and incoherence of human affairs, but they are fragile artefacts. When applied to climate change, the biggest story of all, they seem to crumble.

Climate change is hard to fit into this narrative model: the beginning of our story is written, the middle is coming to a close, but the end is still fiercely debated. The elements that make up the climate story are an uncomfortable shape: science is driven by scepticism, challenge and doubt; journalism likes certainty. Climate change is a long wave, continuous, complex process that may or may not be causally linked to short term, unusual weather events and the human suffering they bring. There are no absolute certainties in this complex chain of causation and scientists are professionally — and rightly — reluctant to confirm anything more solid than a pattern.

The readers scratch their heads and turn away. The Emperor Nero is remembered for fiddling through the burning of just one city. We risk being tuned to the entertainment channel when the global climate passes a tipping point.

The Chinese version of the story follows a slightly different pattern: it is a story told by government that fits into a larger account of recent history and China's place in it, a world in which an innocent

China fell prey in the nineteenth century to malicious exploitation as the ripples from Britain's industrial revolution and western empire-building reached its shores. This story is light on predicted consequences, but has its share of guilty men; none is Chinese, despite the fact that China now emits more CO_2 than any other country. China's industrial revolution, which holds the key to all our futures, is presented as an enabling phenomenon that will finance a future resolution, rather than as a contributor to the problem.

So what kind of story is climate change? Catastrophic narratives have tortured their creators as long as humans have told stories. The Greeks understood how to pare catastrophe down to spare, disciplined drama, creating distilled warnings of the consequences of various human follies, or perhaps of human helplessness as playthings of capricious gods. They do not exactly offer comfort in our present predicament, but they may offer lessons. Cassandra was cursed with clear visions of the future that would never be believed: human society, it seems, is less able to respond to fear than to hope, however tenuous that hope might seem. It is too late to change the beginning or the middle of our story, but perhaps we can still choose the ending.

Four

Chris Hope, economic modeller, University of Cambridge

My own story with climate change stretches back nearly a quarter of a century. In the run-up to the 1992 Earth Summit, the EU wanted to work out what its position should be on climate change and in particular the balance between adaptation and mitigation. So it commissioned some large-scale research that included a model to simulate all the detailed work, which came to be called an 'integrated assessment model'. This model included a summary of the state of knowledge, what uncertainties existed and what the risks were perceived to be. I did this work. We weren't looking at just one view of the future but knew right from the beginning we needed to look at the whole spectrum of climate change outcomes — both the costs and benefits.

This approach is still valid today. Climate change is still a story of risks and risk management, and trying to make sure that you don't get captured by just one single view of the future but remain aware of all the possibilities there might be. Those possibilities include the slight chance that we might get lucky and the climate will not be as bad as we expect it to be — and the slight chance that climate change will be much worse than the mainstream view, with terrible consequences.

The first integrated assessment model I built, called PAGE, came out in 1991. There were updates in 1995, 2002 and 2009, and we're now beginning to think about the next one. My story with climate change has been trying to work through the whole range of costs and benefits. The idea has always been to bring the strongest evidence we can to the decisions that have to be made. One of the imbalances is that, compared with the number of natural scientists involved, there are very few economists working on future risks. You could probably fit the integrated assessment modellers around the world into a minibus. My PAGE model, Bill Nordhaus's DICE model and Richard Tol's FUND are the three main integrated assessment models of the climate.

When preparing the Stern Review on the Economics of Climate Change (2006), Sir Nicholas Stern chose my model to calculate the social cost of carbon. The Stern Review became very influential. The US Environmental Protection Agency has since used my model to identify the social cost of carbon in the US. So the Stern Review marked a big change for me. I stopped feeling like a voice in the wilderness and started to be noticed by policy makers. But that of course meant that I had to ensure that the work wasn't oversold, and be very careful to explain what could and couldn't be achieved by the model. I am not an environmental activist. I am an academic. I'm interested in evidence and representing it as fairly as I can.

Of course, over the entire time I've worked on the topic, emissions of greenhouse gases have continued to rise. At some point we — and I mean the global community — will have to decide if we're going to be serious about all this or not. And maybe we're not. Maybe we pretended to be serious when we thought it wasn't going to cost us very much. But it strikes me that at some point it may become obvious that we are going to have to grasp these issues and actually do something. If you look at the whole range of risks then my prescription is a very clear one: we have to have a strong and increasing and comprehensive price on emissions of greenhouse gases.

The evidence from the modelling I've done is that the price should be of the order of $100 per tonne of carbon dioxide in the EU, higher in the US because they're richer and probably lower in China, India and South America while they're developing — that sort of number. That's an order of magnitude higher than the prices that are placed on greenhouse gases at the moment.

Looking back over the story to date, a high point for me was the production of the Stern Review. The fact that this was something that was commissioned by the Prime Minister and Chancellor of the Exchequer counted for a lot. It has led to some legislation in the UK, such as the Climate Change Act and the Committee on Climate Change. I was pleased to be involved in a small part of it, and to subsequently see the US Environmental Protection Agency do similar work that also drew on my models. But the attention paid to this kind of evidence is typically small. The low point for me has been polarisation of the issue in the US. I am trying to be part of that conversation and talk to a right-leaning constituency that is interested in conservation and in using financial tools to achieve it rather than strict government regulation.

All the recommendations that come out of the kind of modelling that I do fit very naturally into that kind of centre-right or right-wing narrative of economic opportunity as well as into a left-wing narrative of equity. In the future that's what I'd like to see happen: that it stops being a partisan, tribal thing.

Five

George Marshall, Director, Climate Outreach Information Network

Stories are built into the very structure of the brain. As the pioneering cognitive psychologist Seymour Epstein first theorised in the 1970s, and as was subsequently confirmed through neuroimaging, the brain contains two parallel processing systems, the analytic system and the experiential system. Climate science speaks well to the analytic system which deals with abstract symbols, words and numbers. But it is the experiential system that actually compels us to act — and this is driven by emotions, threats, images, intuition and, above all, by stories. As the author Philip Pullman, one of the handful of writers struggling to build stories around climate change, says, 'after nourishment, shelter and companionship, stories are the thing we need most in the world'.

When the scientific data tells us that increasing concentrations of greenhouse gases will increase global temperatures we may try to keep this information safely contained within abstract technical terms that will appeal only to our analytic reasoning. I have come to conclude that many climate scientists actively do this in order to defend themselves against the anxiety generated by their work. But for those of us without the protection of a scientific discipline this unfamiliar, disturbing and unprecedented threat is only made comprehensible in the shape of familiar narratives.

We do not merely respond to stories — we compulsively create them around everything and *anything*. In one famous psychological experiment, when asked to describe an animated film of triangles and squares, people immediately generated a narrative of heroes and villains complete with intentions of altruism, malice, and deceit.

Here lies a problem. Climate change is, among the problems we face, uniquely malleable by interpretive storytelling. It contains no heroes, no enemies, no victims, no motive, no clear beginning nor end, no pivotal event, no climax, no catharsis nor denouement — other than the ones we choose to project onto it. When Barack Obama speaks of 'our moral responsibility to future generations' or the campaigner Bill McKibben writes that 'we have met the enemy and they is Shell', both are presenting us with deliberately constructed narratives shaped by their political worldview. If we are inclined to accept the science, and we share the worldview, we may be inclined to adopt the narrative.

But narratives have their own rules and an emotional appeal that exists independently of their objective truth. Arguments that climate scientists are fiddling the figures in order to secure larger research grants, or that governments and environmentalists are using the issue to extend their control over our personal freedom, are narratives that become, through their familiarity to conservative ears, even more persuasive than the ambiguous and multivalent truth.

Many of the ways that we talk about climate change are more subtle narrative constructions designed to avoid anxiety and personal responsibility. Climate change is constantly framed as a distant problem that will affect animals or other people in faraway countries at some point in the distant future. In Britain, two thirds of people regard climate change as a problem for future generations that will not affect them in their lifetime.

Such stories attain their validity through the social 'proof' of peer transmission rather than the scientific proof of peer review. We follow the social cues of the people we know and trust — our friends, families and preferred media — in the selection of our preferred story of climate change. When we have views that conflict with the social norm around us we choose to suppress them rather than endanger our social allegiances.

It is this suppressed story, this 'climate silence', that has become the most powerful and ubiquitous climate narrative of all. Most people in Britain never discuss climate change outside the closed circle of their friends and family members. A third of people never discuss it with anyone at all. It is an extraordinary lacuna, policed through social disdain and reinforced though averted eyes, awkward pauses, and sudden changes of subject. It allows us to keep our focus on a stable and predictable future whilst ignoring the existential threat that is rapidly gaining pace just around the side of our social blinkers.

The failure to recognise the importance of socially formed narratives is, I have come to believe, the critical flaw in communication strategies around climate change. No amount of disturbing data, scientific reports, vanishing ice, or even, for the near future, extreme weather events will mobilise us to action if we do not have the social permission to share our concerns and a narrative that can give them shape. When we do find the motivation to deal with climate change it will come in the shape of a socially negotiated and widely held story: compelling, irresistible, reinforced through its repetition by those around us. The challenge is to work with each and every constituency to encourage them to give this issue a shape that speaks to their cultural values, fear, hopes and aspirations.

Six

Ruth Padel, poet

My mind immediately goes to *Noye's Fludde*, the opera by Benjamin Britten. Mrs Noah doesn't want to leave home and her friends, her 'Gossips', say it's going to be fine. This flood business is a lot of fuss about nothing. So Noah and her sons have to carry her on board the Ark by force. In Michelangelo's painting of the Flood in the Sistine Chapel, Noah and his family are sailing away but everyone else is frantically climbing trees or desperately sinking beneath the waves.

The science tells us that climate change is going to be like that. Yes, there will be terrible storms and floods. The effects on wildlife, as well as us, will be severe. Take bird migration. Some birds are having to extend their migration routes — and they're already at the limits of their endurance — because the Sahara is increasing in size, and because there are fewer places to nest, take cover and feed en route. Looking forward, there is huge uncertainty: storms, floods and the impacts we're seeing on wildlife today are just the beginning. We don't know how things will go. Climate change is an uncertain, open-ended story.

Climate change is also the story of the human wish to deny. We are so used to the apocalyptic story, the doom-laden story, and we make light of them because making light is how we cope. Climate change deniers take this to an extreme. Setting aside all those who deny because they are invested in polluted energy sources, there are many who are emotionally bound to denial.

Social psychology has a concept called the 'Just World Hypothesis'. People who believe good things happen to you because you're good and bad things happen to other people because they're bad. But when something bad happens to you then you call it an accident. If something good happens to a bad person then it's a 'wrong' thing to happen. Well, the idea that we are responsible for climate change is one that some people just can't psychologically accept.

So the story of climate change is many things and many levels. It is a story of uncertainty. It's a psychological story, a story of denial, a spiritual story. It is constantly evolving.

Seven

James Painter, journalist and researcher

Most societies receive most of their information from the mainstream media so a good place to start is the dominant stories or 'narratives' to which readers and viewers are exposed.

Several studies have shown that the main narratives or 'frames' the media choose (or are given by scientists, scientific reports, government departments or NGOs) are very often ones of negative impacts ('disaster stories') or uncertainty.

This is not surprising, given that many of the impacts the climate models predict are negative — rising sea levels, more droughts in some areas, more extreme weather events in other areas, and so on. Also, as much of climate science concerns the future, it inevitably involves degrees of uncertainty about the timing, pace and severity of possible impacts from a changing climate.

For example, a 2013 study we did at the Reuters Institute for the Study of Journalism (RISJ) of the newspaper coverage of two separate climate change 'stories' (recent reports by the Intergovernmental Panel on Climate Change (IPCC) and reports of Arctic sea ice melt) in newspapers with a combined circulation of 15 million in six countries showed that the messages that readers received were predominantly ones of disaster or uncertainty. This was despite the variety of climate change stories examined, the different media and political contexts of the six countries, and the range of newspapers chosen. The disaster frame or narrative was present in 82% of the 350 articles we looked at, making it the most common frame.

Other studies have come to similar conclusions. For example, a study by the British climate scientist Professor Mike Hulme found that in virtually all the UK print media, the most common tone by far in accounts of the IPCC's 2007 first two reports was alarmist, dominated by the language of catastrophe, fear, disaster and death. Over 75% of the articles fell into this category. He also concluded that the news reporting in that year of the findings of IPCC Working Group 1, which was about the climate system, included 'embellished interpretations' of the impacts that did not appear in the findings of the Working Group itself, but were, rather, 'reported by recycling previously published accounts and reports, or through creative imagination'.

It is to be expected that the media are attracted to doom and gloom stories. But one of the problems with a predominance of disaster narratives is that they are more likely to induce apathy or paralysis through powerlessness or disbelief than motivation and engagement — particularly if they are not accompanied by an action strategy to reduce the perceived risk.

In our RISJ study, uncertainty was the second most common frame after the disaster frame, appearing in 79% of media articles. Journalists follow the prompts from scientists such as those in the IPCC Working Group 1, whose 2013 report highlighted a large number of uncertainties about climate change. As early as the third paragraph, its Summary for Policy Makers explains its concepts of certainty and uncertainty using ranges of probabilities and assigning confidence levels, and the summary goes on to mention 'uncertainty' or 'uncertainties' 36 times.

It is highly laudable that the IPCC scientists are attempting to quantify the uncertainties to help decision making, but there may well be a mismatch with public understanding unless these concepts are explained in a way that the general public can grasp more readily. For example, it is not clear that the public understand what such phrases as '95% certain' or 'very likely' mean in a scientific context. Many fail to make the distinction between what some call 'school science', which is a source of solid facts and reliable understanding, and 'research science' where uncertainty is engrained and is often the impetus for further investigation.

Research carried out both in the USA and the UK suggests that messages of uncertainty can be an obstacle to public engagement. If scientists constantly talk about uncertainty, often the response of the listener is not necessarily apathy but lapsing into an unhappy situation of not knowing how to proceed, and therefore discounting or dodging the problem. Some even get angry when scientists refuse to talk in terms of certainties.

Another problem with highlighting the scientific uncertainties is that some journalists or writers of opinion pieces in the media report the uncertainties extensively, or misreport them, in order to cast doubt on the science. Some media organisations may exaggerate to follow an editorial line of justifying no action on curbing greenhouse gas emissions.

Returning to the RISJ study, it was very apparent that the opportunities that might be presented by addressing climate change are not a common theme for journalists. The opportunity frame was present in around a quarter of all the articles we looked at. However, overwhelmingly these opportunities were those that arose from not doing anything about reducing greenhouse gas emissions (such as oil and gas exploration in the Arctic). Only five articles (less than 2%) in the total sample contained a mention of the opportunities from switching to a low carbon economy.

So the very frames which are not usually seen as enhancing public understanding, engagement or behaviour change are the most common in the media, while positive messages of opportunities arising from climate change, or offering a 'what should we do' approach, have a low presence.

I am pessimistic about a sufficiently ambitious international agreement to curb greenhouse gas emissions being reached in the coming years. But I am much more optimistic about a boom in initiatives at the community, town, city and state levels. That's where much of the innovation and drive will take place. Uncertainty should not be an excuse reason for not taking action, and positive messages in the media could just make a crucial difference.

Eight

Mike Shanahan, biologist and writer

Crack an egg in a pan, turn up the heat and you can witness a kind of magic. In just seconds the viscous egg solidifies. Despite the rising heat, it's the opposite of melting that occurs. I was a teenager when I heard a biology teacher explain this paradox: 'The egg is full of proteins and the heat has denatured them'. *Denatured*. The word was new to me. Twenty-five years later I find it is a fitting descriptor of more than just wayward proteins.

My teacher explained that every protein has a temperature at which it will function best. Too hot or too cold and the protein's shape can buckle or break. It will no longer be able to bond with other chemicals. It will cease to work. I think about that fried egg often when I consider what rising temperatures could mean for the planet.

We know that when people die of heat stroke, part of the problem is that some of their proteins have denatured. Could our cells become our jailors? The proteins inside us and every other living thing vary greatly. Some tolerate heat better than others. Others begin to destabilise at just a couple of degrees warmer than normal. But it is not the average protein that poses a problem. We don't know yet which of the weaker links, those most liable to destabilise in extreme heat, are also critically important — to our food crops for instance.

As the world warms, what will happen to the millions of different proteins in the millions of different species, from spores to sperm whales, soil bacteria to sunflowers? These invisible structures are central to life itself. They give shape not only to hair and to horn but also to hormones and enzymes and DNA. They are the messengers and mechanics that control and correct processes in and between cells. Like the gaps in music that make the beats thrilling, these in-between places are where wonder is born.

It's the same between species. Life is not a zoo of caged individuals living in isolation but a web of shared destiny. And while activists go on about polar bears or other creatures in danger, I am more curious about what climate change could mean for the way species interact and provide us gifts as a result. It's been on my mind since the early years of my career when I lived in a rainforest in Borneo and studied the most fascinating of plants, the strangler figs.

Every one of the 750 or more species of fig trees depends for survival on its own species of tiny wasps that pollinate the flowers. The wasps in turn depend on the figs, the only places in which they can lay their eggs. This mutual reliance combines with the wasps' short lifespans to ensure figs are available year-round, and because of this they sustain more species of birds and mammals than other plants. In return for the fig flesh those creatures disperse the trees' seeds, and provide the same service to thousands of other rainforest plants. These interactions between fig trees and animals help to sustain the great rainforests of the world.

What does this have to do with climate change? Researchers have shown that just a small increase above current temperature levels will shorten a fig wasp's life to just a couple of hours — not enough time to find a fig, pollinate its flowers and lay eggs. No pollination would mean no ripe figs for animals to eat, and this would mean fewer seeds get spread from place to place. Tree species that form a key part of the forest and its capability as an ensemble to lock away carbon are likely to suffer.

The tiny wasps are frail but some of the fig trees' bigger partners are at risk too. They include fruit bats called flying foxes that can carry seeds 50 kilometres or more before pooping them out, making them some of the most effective seed dispersers around. Their vulnerability became clear early in 2014 when thousands of them fell dead from the sky during a blistering heat wave in Queensland, Australia. For both the bats and the fig wasps, the heat was too much. It will have interfered, at a cellular level, with proteins that cooked and then closed for business. These snapshots suggest trouble in store for the fig trees and the forests, whose fates entwine with our own.

Ecology teaches us that no species is an island. It's a lesson our leaders seem to have skipped. It shows us we're all in this together, the fig wasp and the fruit bat, the you and the me. That's what makes the human fingerprints all over climate change all the more ironic. As we develop societies ever more distant from nature to protect ourselves from its wild whims, we risk unleashing upon these *denatured* societies powers we cannot hope to control or even predict.

Nine

Marina Warner, author

Prophecy has become a dominant strain in news reports: experts in various fields are asked, insistently, to predict what the future holds. Politicians announce their plans and promise what they will deliver, and their words often prove to be empty.

Popular publications used to be packed with prophecies: *Old Moore's Almanack* in the nineteenth century was the descendant of pamphlets and broadsheets circulating in print since movable type began, which gave alignments of the planets, news of frogs raining down, thunderbolts, snow in August, and other causes of impending disasters.

This literature was often lurid and aimed to excite alarm, instil fear and trembling and thereby promote god-fearing conduct. It flourished, however, because it simultaneously inspired the shivers of pleasurable dread. But although *Old Moore's Almanack* is still going strong, the tradition of apocalyptic tale-telling has fallen into contempt — as superstitious credulity which an educated audience should laugh at.

The story of climate change, it seems to me, suffers from the (justified) discrediting of such popular, prophetic writing. The scepticism which has been deeply implanted since the age of reason and secular enlightenment has trained us to disregard warnings expressed in apocalyptic language. This is an instance when the underlying blueprint for a narrative is giving the wrong signals, and another model needs to be drafted so that they can be read accurately, and followed. Less general prophecy, more micro-historical case studies.

Another highly popular narrative form dominates the way the effects of climate change are communicated: the *ubi sunt* tradition, which laments lost glories and vanished comforts. This kind of story produces a different effect, in this case, fatalist, which is also less than helpful. Such expressions of grief are intertwined with the vanitas theme — in the Bible, for example, or in the refrain of Villon's famous ballad, 'Mais òu sont les neiges d'antan...?'. It reaches a high point of lyric intensity in 'The Tale of the City of Brass', from the *Arabian Nights*: a group of travellers crossing a vast desert comes across the ruins of one great city after another, and they break down in ecstatic weeping over the wasteland they see stretching all around them. This story echoes in the desolation of Sodom and Gomorrah, Nineveh, Babylon, Jerusalem...

But however gorgeous and passionate the threnodies and elegies might be in such writing, in actual life here and now, weeping won't get us anywhere.

Ten

Chris West, adaptation specialist at the Environment Agency

Several different intellectual frames or stories about climate change co-exist in our society. These different frames impose constraints on how we deal with the issue; these constraints should be managed so we can respond better to the challenges of climate change.

In one frame, climate change is one of among several big issues. For instance Johan Rockström and his colleagues, co-authors of the article 'A safe operating space for humanity', see climate change as one of nine realms where human activity is pushing the planet beyond its limit for maintaining the relatively stable conditions we have seen since the last ice age. These realms are mutually dependent, but only to some extent. Even if we could halt climate change, our assault on planetary supplies of fresh water and biodiversity would still require action. There are limits in the economic and social spheres too that show the same features of interdependency with limited exchangeability.

Another frame or story, promoted by some in the green movement, foregrounds guilt, with individuals or corporations as wrongful actors and nature as the victim. Some greens put more emphasis on the horrors of unmitigated climate change for nature than on practical reasons for reducing emissions. They assume that we all identify with nature, but for many, the natural environment is something remote and irrelevant to their daily business. On the political left, where environmentalism shades into anti-capitalism, it is all too easy to blame climate change on big business (oil companies or financiers). This ignores the role of everyone else on the planet in demanding, buying and using fossil fuel. Thus we are allowed to see climate change as capitalism being unkind to nature, and to ignore our two roles in maintaining capitalism and being part of that nature. This framing narrows our view both of those responsible for and those impacted by climate change, and may narrow our views on where to look for solutions. Should we consider the possibility that someone or some group we don't like might make a large fortune out of providing solutions to climate change?

Another framing tends to highlight uncertainty in climate science, and not always in helpful ways. The climate science community deserves a lot of credit for raising climate change as a globally urgent issue, taking due regard of the actual uncertainties. (In reports of the IPCC, the certainty ascribed to anthropogenic climate change has risen inexorably, so that there is little room now for further increase.)

Among many non-scientists, however, it has often been all too easy to focus on the uncertainties and the continuing academic debates as an excuse to ignore the essential findings of the science and to avoid taking action. The role of the media, in seeking to spice up a rather dull but worthy set of stories by continuing to provoke theatrical disagreement, is moving from mischievous to malign.

The concept of uncertainty is technically useful to scientists in differentiating what they know from what they want to know, and in being honest about the precision of their work, but for the rest of us, we either ignore uncertainty, ascribing too much skill to predictions, or we are misled into doubting even that which is certain. One way to address this problem may be for climate scientists to change the way they describe uncertainty to non-specialists. In terms of action taken to address climate change, would the deliberate imprecision of saying as 'a few degrees warmer' instead of '+2.3°C to +4.1°C' have any negative consequence?

Lastly, it's important to remember that the words that are chosen can affect how an issue is perceived. 'Climate change' is sufficiently anodyne that it finds wide acceptance, but it fails to distinguish between natural variation and unsustainable anthropogenic change, and allows sceptics to claim 'climate has always changed'. 'Changing climate' seems to find some adherents. 'Global warming' has connotations that seem too pleasant for northern Europeans and has the drawback that it describes an incidental side effect of an underlying change. 'Greenhouse effect' sounds too domestic and harmless. The edgier term 'climate chaos' has been seen as too extreme for governments to adopt, and to put undue focus on the negative aspects of unmitigated climate change.

Should we be open to coining new terms for the problem such as 'ignoring the cost of burning fuel' or 'planetary radiation destabilisation' and for possible responses — perhaps, 'keeping fossil fuel underground' or 'running the planet for keeps'?

Eleven

Barry Woods, member of the public and occasional author

I arrived late to the human-made global warming debate. I was, for want of a better phrase, totally climate oblivious. Rio, Kyoto, Bali, IPCC, the UK Climate Change Act, had all passed me by.

I became interested after discovering the Climategate material on a news forum and the media/political hype around 'Saving the Planet' prior to the Copenhagen (COP15) conference. What struck me was: the FoI requests for data that should have been freely given, the apparent incompetence in the handling of data (from my IT professional perspective), and the pressure that scientists appeared to be under to provide a nice, tidy, settled story for the politicians — this last being, I think, the main lesson of Climategate.

The opening video for COP15 was one of the worst offenders for hype. It showed a child running from a rapidly rising ocean and leaping into a tree, screaming for her life. My five-year-old daughter saw this a number of times on the news and had nightmares. Months later she was still asking about that girl. To reassure her, I asked a friend, a UK climate scientist, about sea levels and was told the range from the IPCC figures was 26-59cm, with higher projections being very unlikely.

I started reading the scientific literature, commenting on newspaper articles and blogs and was very quickly labelled as a 'sceptic' or even a 'climate denier', yet I have always thought I was on the side of 'climate science' and scientists and utterly reject any 'anti-science' labels. I have never been sceptical of the field of climate science. On current evidence, I anticipate warming in the range of 1.25-0.5°C as most likely for the 21st century (thus overlapping with the lower end of the range of sensitivity described by the IPCC), but realise others consider a wider range of outcomes possible.

But I am very sceptical of futile and expensive symbolic policies that have no chance of reducing emissions, and of politicians/campaigners who try to silence questioning of policies by citing the authority of 'climate science' or '97% of scientists say'. It was a major concern that the debate was so politicised, with some people named and shamed in 'Denier Halls of Shame' or Denier Disinformation databases, and labelled as part of a fossil fuel denial machine.

Yet the science was settled enough for policymakers decades ago. A range of temperature projections and possible consequence was then, and remains, sufficient to justify action. But politicians could not square the radical demands of total decarbonisation with the growth of developing countries who would not contemplate emission reductions. One added complication was that, because emissions were a consequence of industrialisation and economic growth, a certain environmental worldview automatically rejected technological development as an energy policy option. Thus, the richest nations would seek to reduce emissions whilst the developing world would have no such constraints. In this way, the seed for the failure of the Copenhagen conference was sown years before, prior even to the Kyoto agreement.

I believe that the 21st century will see developing nations bring their citizens out of poverty. I am certain there is no chance politically of a meaningful global agreement to reduce emissions. We should, therefore, concentrate on building resilience and adapting to the possibility of dangerous climate change, or the unlikely risk of catastrophic climate change. Even if this does not occur, we will have saved the lives of millions of the world's poor every year by allowing their economies and personal 'wealth' to grow. By 'wealth' I mean clean water, access to a regular electricity supply, refrigeration, cheap energy, infrastructure — everything that the West takes for granted.

There are climate campaigners convinced that a climate catastrophe is coming and that the public (and even climate scientists) is in denial of this. They will accept no compromise. With this worldview, it is all too easy to dismiss anybody that questions policies as anti-science, 'flat-earth climate sceptics' (the phrase used by then Prime Minister Gordon Brown on the eve of the Copenhagen conference!) or as conspiracy theorists.

If there were no sceptics would climate campaigners be forced to deal with the hard realities that policymakers face, including squaring energy policies with jobs, growth, technological challenges, and the rightful aspirations for a better life for the many, in every part of the world? Calls for radical social change, de-growth and radical decarbonisation would be looked at critically and judged unworkable, leaving policymakers to work on delivering good, rather than 'perfect' results.

Over six million children die from causes related to poverty every year according to Save the Children. We should be ashamed if by 2050 there remain any future poor who might be disproportionately at risk of climate change. Let the politicised rhetoric burn out and allow politicians to concentrate on achieving something in hard reality. I think the campaigners (and perhaps academics and sceptics) need to step aside to make the positive happen more quickly.

A longer version of Barry Woods' contribution can be found at www.unsettledclimate.org/The-Science-Was-Settled-Enough

Contributors
Bibliography
Timeline

Contributors

Alice Bell is a freelance writer and researcher in science, technology, the environment and medicine. She was previously research fellow and head of public engagement at the Science Policy Research Unit, University of Sussex and lecturer in the Science Communication Group at Imperial College London.

Hannah Bird is a freelance project manager and producer for *Culture and Climate Change: Narratives*. For the past eight years she has worked with cultural partners including Cape Farewell, TippingPoint and University of the Arts, London to develop and lead multidisciplinary projects that focus on sustainability and climate change. She was the associate editor on *Expedition*, a Bright Star publication which explored the use of expedition in artistic practice.

Robert Butler is online editor of The Economist's *Intelligent Life* magazine. He was the drama critic of the *Independent on Sunday*, the 'Going Green' columnist for *Intelligent Life*, and co-editor of the Ashden Directory on Environment and Performance. His publications include *The Art of Darkness* (Oberon) and *The Alchemist Exposed* (Oberon).

Tan Copsey is Senior Communications Manager for the Global Commission on the Economy and Climate. Prior to this he worked for BBC Media Action on Climate Asia — the largest ever study of people's experience of climate change, www.chinadialogue.net and www.thethirdpole.net, and online political magazine openDemocracy. Tan has written extensively on the international politics of climate change.

Kris De Meyer is a Research Fellow at King's College London, researching the neuroscience of sensory integration and voluntary movement control. He is also involved in several public engagement projects: he co-produced 'Right Between Your Ears', a documentary about how people believe, and is writing a book about how we judge others.

Nick Drake is a poet and screenwriter. His most recent poetry collection is *The Farewell Glacier* (Bloodaxe, 2012). He has also written the libretto for *Between Worlds*, a new opera for ENO. His screenplay *Romulus My Father* won Best Film at the Australian Film Awards in 2007.

Kate Fletcher is Professor in Sustainability, Design, Fashion at the Centre for Sustainable Fashion, London College of Fashion where she has a broad remit spanning enterprise, education and research. Her strategic leadership permeates the Centre's activities, including its role as co-secretariat to the All Party Parliamentary Group on Ethics and Sustainability in Fashion at the House of Lords.

Caspar Henderson is a writer and editor. *The Book of Barely Imagined Beings: a 21st Century Bestiary* has been highly acclaimed in Britain and the United States, and was shortlisted for the Royal Society science book prize in 2013.

Isabel Hilton is a London-based writer and broadcaster whose work has appeared in the *New Yorker*, the *Guardian*, the *Independent*, the *Sunday Times*, *New York Times*, *El Pais*, *Granta* and many others. She is the founder and editor of www.chinadialogue.net, the world's first fully bilingual Chinese-English web publication on climate and environment, and of www.thethirdpole.net which reports on water in the Himalayan watershed.

Chris Hope is Reader in Policy Modelling at Judge Business School. He was a Lead Author and Review Editor for the Third and Fourth Assessment Reports of the Intergovernmental Panel on Climate Change, and an advisor on the PAGE model to the Stern review on the Economics of Climate Change. In 2007, he was awarded the Faculty Lifetime Achievement Award from the European Academy of Business in Society and the Aspen Institute.

Eleanor Margolies is a writer and theatre-maker and wrote her doctoral thesis on objects and materials in performance. She is founder editor of *Puppet Notebook* magazine. Other publications include *Theatre Materials*, *The Day the Food Ran Out* and *Green Camberwell*.

George Marshall is the founder of the Climate Outreach Information Network, a charity specialising in public engagement around climate change. He writes journalism on the topic and blogs at www.climatedenial.org.

Ruth Padel is an award-winning poet, Teaching Fellow in Poetry at King's College London and first Writer in Residence at the Royal Opera House. Her ten collections have been shortlisted for all major UK prizes. *Learning to Make an Oud in Nazareth*, poems set in and around the Middle East, appears July 2014. See www.ruthpadel.com.

James Painter is Head of the Journalism Fellowship Programme at the Reuters Institute for the Study of Journalism at Oxford University. He is the author of several publications on climate change including *Poles Apart: the international reporting of climate scepticism* and *Climate Change in the Media: reporting risk and uncertainty*.

Kellie C. Payne is a PhD student at the Open University contributing to the Mediating Change project (supervised by Joe Smith and Robert Butler), investigating the relationship between culture and climate change. Previously, she worked in research communications in the area of agriculture and the environment.

Mike Shanahan is a freelance writer and editor. He has a doctorate in rainforest biology and has spent the past ten years doing science journalism

and communications work on environment and development issues. He writes about rainforests, climate change, biodiversity and other environmental topics at his blog www.underthebanyan.wordpress.com.

Bradon Smith is a Research Associate at the Open University and the University of Bath working on the AHRC-funded *Stories of Change* project. He was an AHRC Research Fellow on Climate Change for the Department for Culture, Media and Sport. His background is in English literature, with doctoral research on popular science writing.

Joe Smith is Senior Lecturer in Geography at the Open University. He writes about environmental history, policy and politics, and has worked extensively with broadcasters on global issues. Joe's research tends to be collaborative and interdisciplinary. He is currently leading the AHRC-funded *Earth in Vision* and *Stories of Change* projects. He is co-editor of *Atlas: Geography, Architecture and Change in an Interdependent World* and the *Culture and Climate Change* series.

Zoë Svendsen is a director, researcher and dramaturg. As director of METIS (www.metisarts.co.uk): interdisciplinary projects exploring contemporary political subjects, e.g. China and the global textile industry, capitalism and poker; climate change; virtual reality. As dramaturg: *The Changeling* (Young Vic), *Edward II* (National Theatre) and *Arden of Faversham* (RSC). Zoë lectures in Drama and Performance, English Faculty, University of Cambridge.

Renata Tyszczuk is Senior Lecturer in Architecture at the University of Sheffield. Her research and related art practice explores questions concerning global environmental change and provisionality in architectural thinking. In 2013 she was awarded a British Academy Mid-Career Fellowship. She is co-editor of *Atlas: Geography, Architecture and Change in an Interdependent World* and the *Culture and Climate Change* series.

Marina Warner is a writer of fiction, a critic and a cultural historian. Her most recent book is the award-winning *Stranger Magic: Charmed States & the Arabian*

Nights (2012). *Once Upon a Time: A Short History of Fairy Tale* will be published in October 2014. She is President of the British Comparative Literature Association, a contributing editor to the *London Review of Books*, and a Fellow of All Souls College, Oxford.

Chris West trained as an engineer, and then as a zoologist. He has worked for the British Antarctic Survey, for Jersey and Bristol Zoos, for a Research Council and for the UK Climate Impacts Programme at Oxford University. He is currently a climate change adaptation specialist at the Environment Agency. He is interested in the history of icebreakers; he is an inexpert birdwatcher and fond of wasps.

Barry Woods is an IT manager for a SME following a career in the telecommunications industry. He tweets as @barryjwoods and writes about the policies, economics and science of climate change (man-made & natural) at his blog UnsettledClimate.org and has also written articles for the WattsUpWithThat and Bishop Hill websites. He has a BSc Applied Chemistry (Kingston University) and a MSc Information Systems Engineering (Cybernetics, Reading University).

Bibliography

Adelman, Jeremy (2013) *Worldly Philosopher: The Odyssey of Albert O. Hirschman*, Princeton: Princeton University Press.

Allenby, Braden and Daniel Sarowitz (2011) *The Techno-Human Condition*, Cambridge MA: MIT Press.

Anderson, Kevin et al. (2010) 'Beyond "Dangerous" Climate Change', *Phil. Trans. R. Soc. A*, 13 January 2011 vol. 369 no.1934 pp.20-44.

Applebaum, Noga (2006) 'The Myth of the Innocent Child: The interplay between nature, humanity and technology in contemporary children's science fiction', *The Journal of Children's Literature Studies* vol. 3(2) pp.1-17.

Atwood, Margaret (2006) 'Chicken Little Goes Too Far' in *The Tent*, London: Bloomsbury.

Barnes, Julian (2011), 'A candid view of *Candide*', *The Guardian*, www.theguardian.com/books/2011/jul/01/candide-voltaire-rereading-julian-barnes, 1 July 2011.

Bell, Alice R. (2009) 'The Anachronistic Fantastic: Science, Progress and the Child in 'Postnostalgic' Culture', *International Journal of Cultural Studies*, vol. 12(1) pp. 5-22.

Bell, Alice R. (2013a) 'The Big Bang Fair: a depressing vision of science and engineering', *The Guardian*, www.theguardian.com/science/political-science/2013/mar/18/science-policy1, 18 March 2013.

Bell, Alice R. (2013b) 'What's all the fuss about the precautionary principle?' *The Guardian*, www.theguardian.com/science/political-science/2013/jul/12/precautionary-principle-science-policy, 12 July 2013.

Benedick, Richard (1991) *Ozone Diplomacy: New Directions in Safeguarding the Planet*, Cambridge MA: Harvard University Press.

Bethel, Ellie (2008) *Michael Recycle*, London: Meadowside Children's Books.

Billington, Michael (2011) '*Greenland* — review', The Guardian www.guardian.co.uk/stage/2011/feb/02/greenland-review, 2 February 2011.

Biskup, Agnieszka (2008) *Understanding Global Warming with Max Axiom*, North Mankato, MN: Capstone Press.

Boykoff, Maxwell and Ami Nacu-Schmidt (2013) *World Newspaper Coverage of Climate Change or Global Warming, 2004-2013*. Center for Science and Technology Policy Research, University of Colorado, http://sciencepolicy.colorado.edu/media_coverage.

Bronze, Lewis (1991) *The Blue Peter Green Book*, London: BBC Books.

Buckingham, David (2000) *The Making of Citizens: Young People, News and Politics*, London & New York: Routledge.

Campbell, Colin (1987) *The Romantic Ethic and the Spirit of Modern Consumerism*, Oxford: Blackwell.

Campbell, Lisa (2011) 'Healthy Planet opens Books For Free shops', *The Bookseller*, www.thebookseller.com/news/healthy-planet-opens-books-free-shops.html, 26 June 2011.

Carrington, Damian (2013) 'British children "deeply concerned" about the impact of climate change', *The Guardian*, www.theguardian.com/environment/2013/apr/17/british-children-deeply-concerned-climate-change, 17 April 2013.

Carson, Rachel (1962) *Silent Spring*, London: Hamish Hamilton.

Chabon, Michael (2007) 'After the

Apocalypse', *The New York Review of Books*, 15 February 2007.

Clark, Nigel (2003) 'Turbulent Prospects: Sustaining Urbanism on a Dynamic Planet' in Malcolm Miles and Tim Hall (eds.) *Urban Futures*, London: Routledge, pp.182–193.

Clark, Nigel (2011) *Inhuman Nature: Sociable Life on a Dynamic Planet*. London: Sage.

Coveney, M. (2011) 'Greenland', 2 February 2011, *Whatsonstage* www.whatsonstage.com/reviews/theatre/london/E8831296639794/Greenland.html.

Crown, Sarah (2005) 'Paper Weight', *The Guardian*, http://blogs.guardian.co.uk/culturevulture/archives/2005/11/10/paper_weight.html, 10 November 2005.

Dr Seuss (2009) *The Lorax Eco Edition*, London: HarperCollins.

Fermor, Patrick Leigh (2004) *A Time of Gifts: On Foot to Constantinople: From the Hook of Holland to the Middle Danube*, London: John Murray.

Foreman, Michael (1972) *Dinosaurs and All that Rubbish*, Harmondsworth: Puffin Books.

Fyfe, Aileen (ed.) (2003) *Science For Children*, Bristol: Thoemmes Press.

Gauntlett, David (1996) *Video Critical: Children, the Environment and Media Power*, Luton: John Libby Media.

Gauntlett, David (2011) *Making is Connecting: The social meaning of creativity, from DIY and knitting to YouTube and Web 2.0*, London: Polity.

Goldenberg, Suzanne (2012) 'US military warned to prepare for consequences of climate change' *The Guardian*, www.theguardian.com/world/2012/nov/09/us-military-warned-climate-change, 9 November 2012.

Greenpeace International (2005) 'Harry Potter and the half-good prints', www.greenpeace.org/international/en/news/features/harry-potter-111/, 13 July 2005.

Hansen, James (2013) *A scientist's view of the climate crisis*, public lecture at the LSE, 16 May, video: www.lse.ac.uk/GranthamInstitute/events/Multimedia/video-james-hansen-scientist-view-of-climate-crisis.aspx.

Hemming, Sarah. (2011) 'Greenland, National Theatre, London', *The Financial Times* www.ft.com/cms/s/2/97aab5f0-307d-11e0-9de3-00144feabdc0.html#axzz1mHfcxlBO, 4 February 2011.

Henderson, Caspar (2012) *The Book of Barely Imagined Beings*, London: Granta.

Henderson, Caspar (2013) 'Growing Up in the Anthropocene' http://fivebooks.com/interviews/caspar-henderson-on-growing-anthropocene.

Hickman, Leo (2011) 'Fracking company targets US children with colouring book' *The Guardian*, www.theguardian.com/environment/blog/2011/jul/14/gas-fracking-children-colouring-book, 14 July 2011.

Huet, Marie-Helene (2012) *The Culture of Disaster*, Chicago: University of Chicago Press.

Intergovernmental Panel on Climate Change, First Report (1990) www.ipcc.ch

Jenkins, Henry (2006) *Convergence Culture: Where Old and New Media Collide*, New York & London: New York University Press.

Kahneman, Daniel (2011) *Thinking Fast and Thinking Slow*, London and New York: Penguin.

Kant, Immanuel ([1756] 1964) 'History and Physiography of the Most Remarkeable Cases of the Earthquake Which Towards the End of the Year 1755 Shook a Great Part of the Earth,' in *Four Neglected Essays by Immanuel Kant*, trans. John Richardson, ed. Stephen Palmquist, Hong Kong: Philopsychy Press.

Kinder, Masha (1995) 'Home Alone in the 90s: Generational War and Transgenerational Address in American Movies, Television and Presidential Politics', in Cary Bazalgette & David Buckingham (eds) *In Front of the*

Children: Screen Entertainment and Young Audiences, London: BFI Publishing, pp. 75-91.

Kingsolver, Barbara (2012) *Flight Behaviour*, London: Faber and Faber.

Krugman, Paul (2013) 'Gambling With Civilisation', *New York Review of Books*, www.nybooks.com/articles/archives/2013/nov/07/climate-change-gambling-civilization, 7 November 2013.

Kyoto Protocol http://unfccc.int/kyoto_protocol/items/2830.php

Latour, Bruno (2011) 'From Multiculturalism to Multinaturalism: What Rules of Method for the New Socio-Scientific Experiments?' *Nature and Culture* Volume 6, Number 1, Spring 2011, pp. 1-17.

Lomborg, Bjørn (2009) 'Scared silly over climate change', *The Guardian*, www.theguardian.com/commentisfree/cif-green/2009/jun/15/climate-change-children, 15 June 2009.

Meadows, Donella H., Meadows D.L., Randers J. and Behrens W.W III (1972) *The Limits to Growth — A Report on the Club of Rome's Project on the Predicament of Mankind*, New York: Universe Books.

Meadows, Donella H. (1999) 'Chicken Little, Cassandra and the real wolf: so many ways to think about the future', *Whole Earth* Spring, vol. 96, Spring, pp. 106-111.

McCarthy, Cormac (2009) *The Road*, London: Picador.

Mendlesohn, Farah (2007) 'With Meccano to the Stars!', in Pat Pinset (ed) *Time Everlasting: Representations of past, present and future in children's literature*, Staffordshire: Pied Piper Publishing, pp. 215-231.

Miller, Joshua Rhett (2011) 'Energy Company Abandons 24-Page Coloring Book on Fracking Featuring Friendly Fracosaurus', Fox News, www.foxnews.com/us/2011/07/14/fracking-coloring-book-by-talisman-energy-blasted-by-critics/?cmpid=cmty_email_Gigya_Energy_Company_Abandons_24-Page_Coloring_Book_on_Fracking_

Featuring_%27Friendly_Fracosaurus%27, 14 July 2011.

Morpurgo, Michael (2005) *Kensuke's Kingdom*, London: Egmont.

Neiman, Susan (2002) *Evil in Modern Thought: An Alternative History of Philosophy* Princeton NJ: Princeton University Press.

Nodleman, Perry (1985) 'Out There In Children's Science Fiction: Forward into the Past', *Science Fiction Studies*, vol. 12, pp. 285-295.

Obama, Barack (2013) 'Remarks by the President on Climate Change' Georgetown University Washington D.C., www.whitehouse.gov/the-press-office/2013/06/25/remarks-president-climate-change, 25 June 2013.

Odell, Michael (2009) 'So, how many trees have you planted, Daddy?' *The Observer*, www.theguardian.com/environment/2009/feb/01/ethicalliving-family, 1 February 2009.

Painter, James (2011) *Poles Apart: The International Reporting of Climate Scepticism*. Oxford: Reuters Institute for the Study of Journalism.

Porritt, Jonathan (1991) *Captain Eco and the Fate of the Earth*, London: Dorling Kindersley.

Purves, Libby. (2011) 'Greenland at the Lyttelton, SE1', *The Times* www.thetimes.co.uk/tto/arts/stage/theatre/article2896457.ece, 2 February 2011.

Readman, Jo (2006) *George Saves the World by Lunchtime*, London: Eden Project.

Reay, David (2009) *Your Planet Needs You*, London: Macmillan.

Rich, Motoko (2011) 'Fairies, Witches and Supply and Demand', *New York Times*, www.nytimes.com/2011/08/21/opinion/fairies-witches-and-supply-and-demand.html, 20 August 2011.

Rockström, Johan et al. (2009) 'A safe operating space for humanity', *Nature* 461:472-475. doi:10.1038/461472a.

Rose, Jacqueline (1994) *The Case of Peter Pan: Or the Impossibility of Children's Literature*, Basingstoke: Macmillan.

Rousseau, Jean-Jacques (1756) 'Lettre à Voltaire' 18 August 1756, in *Oeuvres completes*, ed. Henri Gouhier (Paris: Gallimard, 1969).

Scranton, Roy (2013) 'Learning How to Die in the Anthropocene', *New York Times*, 10 November 2013.

Self, Will (2007) *The Book of Dave: A Revelation of the Recent Past and the Distant Future*, London: Penguin.

Serres, Michel (1995) *The Natural Contract*, Ann Arbor: University of Michigan Press.

Shepherd, Jessica (2011) 'Climate change should be excluded from curriculum, says adviser', *The Guardian*, www.theguardian.com/education/2011/jun/12/climate-change-curriculum-government-adviser, 12 June 2011.

Shepherd-Barr, Kirsten (2006) *Science on stage: from Doctor Faustus to Copenhagen*, Woodstock, Oxfordshire: Princeton University Press.

Shirky, Clay (2010) *Cognitive Surplus: Creativity and Generosity in a Connected Age*, London: Allen Lane.

Sierz, Aleks (2011a) 'Greenland, National Theatre: An ambitious four-way exploration of climate change remains too cool', *The Arts Desk*, www.theartsdesk.com/theatre/greenland-national-theatre, 1 February 2011.

Sierz, Aleks (2011b) 'Greenland', *The Stage*, www.thestage.co.uk/reviews/review.php/31144/greenland, 2 February 2011.

Sierz, Aleks (2011c) *Rewriting the Nation: British Theatre Today*, London: A&C Black.

Smith, Joe (2011) 'Why Climate Change is different: six elements that are shaping the new cultural politics' in Butler et al. (eds.) *Culture and Climate Change: Recordings* (Cambridge: Shed); pp. 17–22.

Spencer, Charles (2011) 'Greenland, National Theatre', *The Telegraph*, 2 February 2011.

Stirling, Andy (2013) 'Why the precautionary principle matters', www.theguardian.com/science/political-science/2013/jul/08/precautionary-principle-science-policy, 8 July 2013.

Talen, Billy (2013) *The End of the World*, New York: O/R Books.

Taylor, Paul (2011) 'Greenland, National Theatre: Lyttleton, London', *The Independent*, 3 February 2011.

Voltaire, Poème sur le désastre de Lisbonne (1756); 'Poem on The Lisbon Disaster' in David Wootton (ed.) *Candide and Related Texts* (Indianapolis: Hackett Publishing Company, 2000); pp. 99–108.

Voltaire (1759) *Candide ou l'Optimisme*, *Candide or Optimism*, trans. Roger Pearson, *Candide and Other Stories* (London, Everyman's Library, 1992).

Weisman, Alan (2008) *The World Without Us*. London: Virgin Books.

Wesley, Mary (1969) *The Sixth Seal*, London: Macmillan.

Wright, David (2005) 'Commodifying Respectability: Distinctions at work in the Bookshop', *Journal of Consumer Culture*, vol. 5(3): pp. 295–314.

Winston, Andrew (2013) 'Obama Gave a Monumental Climate Change Speech, But It's Still Not Enough', Harvard Business Review Blog Network; http://blogs.hbr.org/2013/06/obama-gave-a-monumental-climate-speech-but-its-still-not-enough, 26 June 2013.

Winterson, Jeanette (2008) *The Stone Gods*, London: Penguin.

Zalasiewicz, Jan (2008) *The Earth After Us: What Legacy will Humans Leave in the Rocks?* Oxford: Oxford University Press.

Zalasiewicz, Jan. et al. (2009) 'Stratigraphy of the Anthropocene', *Philosophical Transactions of the Royal Society* A (2011) 369, pp. 1036–1055. doi:10.1098/rsta.2010.0315.

Timeline

c.850

Severe drought exacerbated by soil erosion leads to collapse of Central American city states and the end of the Classic Maya civilization.

1200s

Collapse of the Ancient Pueblo or Anasazi civilisation in Southwest USA attributed to drought and deforestation.

1250

Start of the Little Ice Age, a stadial period within the interglacial warm period which ends around 1850.

1350

Western Settlement in Greenland abandoned, possibly due to the deteriorating climate caused by the onset of the Little Ice Age.

1453

Eruption of Kuwae in the Pacific. The resulting climatic effects are recorded in the history of the Ming Dynasty and in the chronicles of the days leading up to the fall of Constantinople.

1608

The first recorded frost fair on the Thames; the Thames froze for weeks at a time in many winters between the mid-14th and 19th century, in the period known as the 'Little Ice Age'.

1661

In *Fumifugium, or, The Inconveniencie of the Aer and Smoak of London Dissipated*, John Evelyn proposes remedies for London's air pollution including public parks and the planting of flowers and fragrant trees. In *Sylva, or a Discourse of Forest Trees* (1664) he encourages landowners to plant trees to supply the navy.

1667

Milton's *Paradise Lost* describes the tilt in the Earth's axis affecting the climate: 'Some say he bid his Angels turne ascanse/ The Poles of Earth twice ten degrees and more/From the Suns Axle [...] to bring in change/Of Seasons to each Clime; else had the Spring/ Perpetual smil'd on Earth...' (Book 10).

1712

Invention of the atmospheric steam engine by Thomas Newcomen (later improved upon by James Watt) leading to the Industrial Revolution and increased emission of greenhouse gases due to burning coal, steam railways and land clearance.

1755

Massive earthquake destroys Lisbon and shakes belief in benevolent nature among Enlightenment thinkers.

1770

Failure of the monsoons in the late 1760s contributes to the Bengal famine of 1770 in which 10 million people die.

1776

The History of the Decline and Fall of the Roman Empire by Edward Gibbon is 'the first systematic attempt to relate climatic factors to the declining fortunes of a major civilisation' (Hulme, 2009: 28).

1783

A volcanic eruption in Iceland causes crop failure and hunger.

1800–1870

Level of carbon dioxide gas (CO_2) in the atmosphere, as later measured in ancient ice, is about 290 ppm (parts per million). Mean global temperature (1850–1870) is about 13.6 °C.

1803

Luke Howard publishes *Essay on the Modification of Clouds*. His classification and naming of clouds influences

Shelley, Constable and Ruskin.

1815

Eruption of Mount Tambora on the island of Sumbawa (Indonesia) causes severe climate abnormalities in the following year.

1816

The Year Without a Summer (also known as the Poverty Year). Average global temperatures decreased by 0.4-0.7°C; snow fell in midsummer; crops failed and livestock died, resulting in major food shortages across the northern hemisphere.

1824

Fourier calculates that the Earth would be far colder if it lacked an atmosphere.

1836

'Nature' by Ralph Waldo Emerson, an essay that influences Henry David Thoreau, Emily Dickinson and other writers later described as Transcendentalists.

1842

'The Rain King, or a Glance into the Next Century' by Eliza Leslie: in a fictional 1942, the Rain King offers weather on demand to the residents of the Philadelphia area.

1845-1857

Unusually wet weather in northern Europe causes crop failures. Worst affected is the potato, on which both Ireland

and Scotland are heavily dependent. A million starve or die of disease in the Irish Famine and two million emigrate within a decade. Food shortages elsewhere in Europe lead to civil unrest and the revolutions of 1848.

1854

Walden; Or, Life in the Woods by Henry David Thoreau records his experience of simple living and self-sufficiency.

1859

John Tyndall correctly measures the relative infrared absorptive powers of the gases nitrogen, oxygen, water vapour, carbon dioxide, ozone, methane. He concludes that water vapour is the strongest absorber of radiant heat in the atmosphere and is the principal gas controlling air temperature. Tyndall is the first to prove that the Earth's atmosphere has a greenhouse effect.

1864

Man and Nature by George Perkins Marsh — an early but influential work documenting human effects on the environment.

1873

Antonio Stoppani acknowledges the increasing impact of humanity on the Earth's systems, referring to the 'anthropozoic era'.

1885

After London by Richard

Jefferies — an early example of 'post-apocalyptic fiction' which imagines a Britain depopulated after an unspecified catastrophe, and in which nature has reclaimed the land.

1889

Writer and naturalist John Muir begins the campaign to save the Yosemite region in California from exploitation. His articles in *Century Magazine* lead to a bill in Congress to expand federal protection, and ultimately to the creation of the National Park Service in 1916.

1890-1920

Composers including Delius, Vaughan Williams and Percy Grainger contribute to the English Folk Revival, celebrating an endangered rural life. Its detractors called it 'cowpat music'.

1896

The National Trust is founded by Octavia Hill, Robert Hunter and Hardwicke Rawnsley to conserve threatened coastline, countryside and buildings. They are supported by John Ruskin, artist, writer and advocate of conservation measures including town and country planning, green belts and smokeless zones.
—
Arrhenius publishes the first calculation of global warming from human emissions of CO_2.

1897

Chamberlin produces a

model for global carbon exchange including feedbacks.

1915

The Origin of Continents and Oceans by Alfred Wegener introduces tectonic plate theory, arguing that 300 million years ago the continents formed a single landmass.

1920–1925

Opening of Texas and Persian Gulf oil fields.

1925

The Professor's House by Willa Cather describes the abandoned cities of the Anasazi.

1926

Russian scientist Vladimir Vernadsky publishes theory of the integration of the biosphere, or living matter, and the earth's geological processes.

1936

Noah and the Waters by Cecil Day-Lewis imagines the inundation of contemporary Britain.

1945

End of Pacific war and second world war, with heavy bombardment, genocide, and explosions. Nuclear warfare occurs for the first time when Hiroshima and Nagasaki are bombed. Nuclear tests are subsequently performed by the United States, Soviet Union, India, Pakistan, China, North Korea, the United Kingdom, and France. Above-ground detonations continue

until the Partial Test Ban Treaty is signed in 1963.

1946

Founding of the Soil Association in the UK.

1951

The Day of the Triffids by John Wyndham: bioengineered plants — mobile, carnivorous, poisonous — escape into the wild.

1952

Smog — a mixture of smoke and fog — is blamed for the deaths of 1,000 Londoners, forcing the British Parliament to pass the Clean Air Act.

1953

The Man Who Planted Trees, by Jean Giono, a fable of the reforestation of a French valley.
—
In January, a storm tide devastates the coasts of East Anglia and the Netherlands, killing more than 2,000 people.

1955

Patrick Hadley's cantata *Fen and Flood*, arranged for four-part chorus by Vaughan Williams, a history of East Anglia and its relationship with the sea, responds to the 1953 floods.

1956

The Death of Grass by John Christopher: a virus that wipes out grass and crops decimates Asia, causing mass starvation and riots, and eventually hits Britain.
—

Mysterious illnesses in the small town of Minimata in Japan are found to be caused by mercury poisoning from industrial pollution. Attempts at a cover-up by business and government create the world's first environmental scandal. David Holman's 1972 play *Drink the Mercury* portrays the aftermath of the poisoning.

1957

The International Geophysical Year helps to establish a global scientific community concerned with exploring planetary processes. This lays the ground for later studies that point to human-induced climate change.

1958

Benjamin Britten's opera *Noye's Fludde (Noah's Flood)* is performed in Orford Church, Suffolk, as part of the Aldeburgh Festival, with the English Opera Group and a local cast. The opera partly responds to the 1953 floods in East Anglia.

1960

Charles David Keeling accurately measures CO_2 in the earth's atmosphere and detects an annual rise. The level is 315 ppm. Mean global temperature (five-year average) is 13.9 °C.
—
In 'Dome over Manhattan' Richard Buckminster Fuller and Shoji Sadao sketch a huge dome covering a large proportion of Manhattan island to create a climatically self-sufficient city.

1962

Silent Spring by biologist Rachel Carson popularises understanding of the impact of pesticides on wildlife and humans. The grassroots environmental movement the book inspires leads to the creation of the Environmental Protection Agency in the United States.

—

Peter and Eileen Caddy and Dorothy Maclean found the Findhorn community in Scotland.

—

The Drowned World by J.G. Ballard imagines a flooded London after ice caps melt and sea levels rise.

1963

US Congress passes the first Clean Air Act.

1966

Founding of *Resurgence* magazine, which explores ecology, spirituality and the arts. Early contributors include E.F. Schumacher, Leopold Kohr and John Seymour.

1967

The Torrey Canyon oil tanker breaks open off the coast of Cornwall — the first major oil spill.

1968

The Whole Earth Catalog provides a handbook for self-sufficiency, listing equipment, tools and machinery, alongside articles on topics including organic farming, resource depletion, solar power, recycling and wind energy.

—

Elisabeth Beresford

publishes the first Wombles book, which in 1973 becomes a popular UK children's TV show. The Wombles' theme song includes the lines 'Making good use of the things that we find,/Things that the everyday folks leave behind' and their motto is 'Make Good Use of Bad Rubbish'.

1969

Friends of the Earth founded in the USA.

—

Operating Manual for Spaceship Earth by Buckminster Fuller popularises the phrase 'Spaceship Earth' to describe the planet's finite resources.

1970

First Earth Day.

—

The Ecologist magazine founded.

1971

Greenpeace founded in Canada.

—

The Lorax by Dr Seuss describes what happens when a forest of Truffula trees is chopped down.

—

Design for the Real World by Victor Papanek draws attention to the damage caused by corporations and consumer culture and provokes debate about the ethical responsibilities of design practice.

—

Not Not Not Not Not Enough Oxygen, a play by Caryl Churchill set in London 2010.

—

Diet for a Small Planet by Frances Moore Lappé

exposes the waste in US grain-fed meat production.

—

What's Going On, a concept album with a strong environmental theme, by Marvin Gaye.

1972

The United Nations Conference on the Human Environment (the Stockholm Conference) produces the first document in international law to recognise the right to a healthy environment. The United Nations Environment Programme is formed. Many in developing countries accused environmentalists in the developed world of 'pulling up the ladder behind them'.

—

Droughts in Africa, Ukraine and India cause world food crisis.

—

The American meteorologist Edward Lorenz presents a paper, 'Predictability: Does the Flap of a Butterfly's Wings in Brazil Set Off a Tornado in Texas?' pointing out the chaotic nature of climate systems and the possibility of sudden shifts.

—

Memoirs of a Survivor by Doris Lessing, a dystopian novel about the breakdown of society.

—

Mike Reynolds builds his first 'earthship', the Thumb House, from discarded materials and forms the architectural practice Earthship Biotecture to promote low-impact self-servicing dwellings.

—

US Congress passes Federal Water Pollution

Control Amendments, later known (with additional legislation) as the Clean Water Act.

—

The Club of Rome publishes *The Limits to Growth*, a report about the computer modelling of exponential economic and population growth with finite resources.

1973
Oil embargo and price rise: the first 'energy crisis'.

—

Small is Beautiful by E.F. Schumacher challenges the dominant trend towards globalisation.

—

The Ecology Party (later renamed the Green Party) founded in Britain.

—

Z for Zachariah by Robert C. O'Brien, a post-apocalyptic novel for young people.

1974
The Comedy of Survival: Joseph Meeker proposes that the truly ecological genre is comedy.

1975
Investigation of trace gases in the stratosphere leads to discovery of the danger airplane emissions pose to ozone layer.

—

In BBC TV comedy drama *The Good Life* Tom and Barbara Good give up the rat race to become self-sufficient.

—

The Monkey Wrench Gang, a novel by Edward Abbey, describes sabotage of environmentally damaging activities in the American Southwest; a possible

inspiration for the founding of Earth First! in 1980.

1976
Studies show that CFCs, methane and ozone can make a serious contribution to the greenhouse effect; in 1977 the US bans CFCs from aerosol spray cans.

—

The Complete Book of Self-Sufficiency by John Seymour.

1977
Scientific opinion converges on global warming as the chief climate risk in next century.

—

Wangari Maathai founds Kenya's Green Belt Movement. By 1992 the movement has planted over seven million saplings, proving the effectiveness of grassroots organisation and 'appropriate technology' (a term popularised by Schumacher). Maathai receives the Nobel Peace Prize in 2004.

1978
The Ennead by Jan Mark, a novel for young people in which a depleted, uninhabitable earth has been abandoned.

1979
Second oil 'energy crisis'.

—

Gaia by James Lovelock puts forward the idea that the biosphere is self-regulating.

1980
The World Conservation Strategy is published, becoming the basis for national conservation plans in many developing nations.

—

Radical direct action group Earth First! is formed by Arizona desert activists Dave Foreman, Howie Wolke and Mike Roselle.

1981
The Revenge of Samuel Stokes by Penelope Lively: ghosts of a historical garden haunt a new housing estate, culminating in the return of an ornamental lake.

1985
The UN Environment Programme, World Meteorological Organization and the International Council of Scientific Unions conference at Villach, Austria. Scientists from 29 developed and developing countries assess the role of increased carbon dioxide and other greenhouse gases and aerosols on climate changes and associated impacts. The conference is also significant in proposing that the state of scientific knowledge justified political action. Its joint statement opens: 'As a result of the increasing concentrations of greenhouse gases, it is now believed that in the first half of the next century a rise of global mean temperature could occur which is greater than any in man's history'.

—

An 'ozone hole' above Antarctica is discovered by British scientists, and is explained in terms of release of CFCs by industry and consumer products.

1986

Slow Food movement founded by Carlo Petrini in Italy.
—
In the USSR, nuclear reactor number 4 explodes in Chernobyl, Ukraine. Cultural responses include Christa Wolf's novel *Störfall* (Accident) and the play *Sarcophagus* by Vladimir Gubaryev, the science editor of *Pravda*.

1987

Gro Harlem Brundtland, Norwegian Prime Minister, defines sustainable development as 'development which meets the needs of the present without compromising the ability of future generations to meet their own needs'.
—
The Montreal Protocol, an international agreement to phase out ozone-depleting chemicals, CFCs, is signed by the main industrial countries, demonstrating that fast and effective action on a global environmental issue is possible.

1988

Coverage of global warming leaps up the news agenda following record heat and droughts.
—
Dr James Hansen testifies to US Congress, saying that he could state 'with 99 per cent confidence' that there was a long-term warming trend.
—
Toronto Conference on the Changing Atmosphere calls for strict, specific limits on greenhouse gas emissions. This was the first major international meeting bringing governments and scientists together to discuss action on climate change. Industrialised countries pledged to voluntarily cut CO_2 emissions by 20% by the year 2005. This meeting was also critical in the establishment of the Intergovernmental Panel on Climate Change.
—
UK Prime Minister Thatcher is first world leader to call for action on global warming.
—
Ice core and biology studies confirm living ecosystems give climate feedback by way of methane, which could accelerate global warming.
—
Intergovernmental Panel on Climate Change (IPCC) established to review and report on international science, impacts and responses to climate change.
—
The assassination by ranchers of Chico Mendes, leader of Brazil's rubber tappers' union, and a prominent figure in the movement to save the rainforest from illegal logging. Mendes' death was one of an estimated 1,700 resulting from land disputes in Brazil over two decades.

1989

The End of Nature by Bill McKibben.
—

Breakthrough voting levels of 15% for the UK Green Party in the European Parliament elections.

1990

IPCC publishes First Assessment Report. It finds that the planet warmed by 0.5 degrees C in the 20th century, and warns that only strong measures to halt rising greenhouse gas emissions will prevent serious global warming.

1991

Researchers at the Centre for the Study of Environmental Change, Lancaster, look at environmental issues as sociological, cultural, philosophical phenomena, rather than as a purely 'physical' or 'policy' set of issues and problems.
—
Ken Saro-Wiwa founds Nigeria's Movement for the Survival of the Ogoni People in reaction to Shell's oil drilling and extensive pollution in the Niger river delta. The country's military dictators respond to massive demonstrations with threats, intimidation and arrest of the movement's leaders and, in 1995, their execution.

1992

United Nations Conference on Environment and Development in Rio de Janeiro produces UN Framework Convention on Climate Change, but US blocks calls for serious action. Also known as Earth Summit, Rio Summit or Rio Conference.

1993

Greenland ice cores suggest that great climate changes (at least on a regional scale) can occur in the space of a single decade.

—

In Tony Kushner's play *Angels in America: Millennium Approaches*, an angel descends to earth through a hole in the ozone layer.

—

In the novel *Gridlock*, by Ben Elton, a city chokes on carbon monoxide.

—

The poet laureate, Ted Hughes, edits *Sacred Earth Dramas*, an anthology of plays inspired by the Earth Summit.

1995

Second IPCC report detects 'signature' of human-caused greenhouse effect warming, and declares that serious warming is likely in the coming century.

—

Reports of the breaking up of Antarctic ice shelves and other signs of warming in polar regions begin to affect public opinion.

1997

International conference produces Kyoto Protocol, setting targets for industrialized nations to reduce greenhouse gas emissions if enough nations sign a treaty (rejected by the US Senate in advance).

—

Cities for a Small Planet, by architect Richard Rogers.

1998

Average global temperatures for the year are the warmest on record.

2000

Launch of the Ashden Directory, an online magazine about environmentalism and performing arts, with a database of productions since 1893 that have environmental themes.

—

The conference 'Between Nature: Explorations in ecology and performance' at Lancaster University is the first international event bringing together performers, academics and activists.

—

The Song of the Earth, a study of literature and environment by Jonathan Bate.

—

The Theft of Sita, a shadow theatre performance presenting the destruction of Indonesian rainforest through the ancient Ramayana epic.

2001

Third IPCC report states that global warming unprecedented since end of last ice age is 'very likely'.

2002

Larsen B ice shelf disintegrates.

2003

A summer heatwave kills 30,000 people in Europe. Media reports associate the highest temperatures recorded in 500 years with climate change.

—

The first Cape Farewell expedition of artists and scientists sails to the High Arctic to study global warming.

—

The Long Summer: How Climate Changed Civilisation by Brian Fagan.

Oryx and Crake by Margaret Atwood, a post-apocalyptic novel exploring the consequences of genetic engineering.

—

Observations raise concern that collapse of ice sheets can raise sea levels faster than most had believed.

2004

The Day After Tomorrow, a Hollywood blockbuster that depicts a rapid transition to a new ice age.

—

The Death of Environmentalism: Global Warming Politics in a Post-Environmental World, by Michael Shellenberger and Ted Nordhaus, rejects the vision of the 1970s environmental movement and calls for radical rethinking of its aims.

—

The Noah's Ark Project details the impact of climate change on cultural heritage sites in Europe.

—

Earthquake causes large tsunamis in the Indian Ocean, killing nearly a quarter of a million people.

—

Public Smog is opened as an 'atmospheric park' created by artist Amy Balkin through the use of financial, political, and legal methods, to 'highlight the complexities and contradictions of current environmental protocols'.

2005

Avoiding Dangerous Climate Change Symposium convened by the UK government to bring together the latest research on how to achieve the objective of the 1992 United Nations Framework Convention on Climate Change.

—

Kyoto treaty goes into effect, signed by major industrial nations except US.

—

Hurricanes Katrina, Rita, and Wilma cause widespread destruction and environmental harm to coastal communities in the US Gulf Coast region, especially the New Orleans area and spur debate over impact of global warming on storm intensity.

—

The Thunder Mutters:101 Poems for the Planet, a collection of poems edited by Alice Oswald.

—

Collapse by Jared Diamond presents climate change as one of the five factors that drive social collapse.

—

First TippingPoint meeting of artists and scientists.

—

Lines of Defence, site-specific art installation by Bettina Furneé addressing coastal erosion, Bawdsey, England.

—

English Heritage report (with UCL Centre for Sustainable Heritage): *Climate Change and the Historic Environment*.

—

Northsoutheastwest

exhibition of Magnum photographers, organised by the Climate Group.

—

Royal Society of the Arts 'Arts and Ecology' website launched (actively maintained until 2010).

2006

An Inconvenient Truth, a film presented by Al Gore.

—

The Stern Review on the Economics of Climate Change. Its main conclusion is that the benefits of strong, early action on climate change considerably outweigh the costs.

—

We Turned on the Light by Orlando Gough and his choral group, The Shout, commissioned for the Proms with libretto about climate change by Caryl Churchill.

—

Syriana, a political thriller about corruption in the global oil industry.

—

The Canary Project founded in the United States.

—

Transition Town Totnes founded.

—

In *Field Notes from a Catastrophe* Elizabeth Kolbert describes the impact of climate change on people in the Netherlands, Iceland and Alaska.

—

And While London Burns, a 'soundtrack for the era of climate change', an operatic audio tour by PLATFORM of institutions in London's financial district.

—

Climate Change: Cultural

Change symposium by Helix Arts, at World Summit on Arts and Culture.

—

Land, Art anthology, edited by Max Andrews (RSA Arts and Ecology).

—

The Road, by Cormac McCarthy, a post-apocalyptic novel about a father and son, is widely seen as a view of the future after extreme climate change.

—

UNESCO World Heritage Centre report: *Predicting and Managing the Effects of Climate Change on World Heritage*.

—

National Trust (UK) report: *Forecast — Changeable? Climate Change Impacts around the National Trust*.

—

The Ship: The Art of Climate Change, the Cape Farewell exhibition at the Natural History Museum, London, and touring nationally and internationally thereafter.

2007

The fourth IPCC report confirms the human cause of global warming, warns that serious effects of warming have become evident, and outlines the economic and lifestyle changes necessary to mitigate those impacts. The reports state that the cost of reducing emissions would be far less than the damage they will cause.

—

Greenland and Antarctic ice sheets and Arctic Ocean sea-ice cover found to be shrinking faster than expected.

—

Floods in June force thousands in England from their homes.

—

Monsoon flooding in the Indian subcontinent causes 14 million Indians and 5 million Bangladeshis to leave their homes.

—

2,000 protestors camp on the site of a proposed third runway at Heathrow airport.

—

Arcola Energy aims to make the Arcola Theatre in London carbon neutral.

—

The National Theatre in London commits itself to reducing its use of gas and electricity by 20% over three years.

—

The Eleventh Hour, a film starring Leonardo DiCaprio.

—

Invisible Bonfires, a performance by Forkbeard Fantasy.

—

The Low Carbon Show, a regular radio programme on Resonance FM.

—

Live Earth global music event sees Al Gore and colleagues promoting action on climate change.

—

The Most Terrifying Video You'll Ever See 2, made by a US science teacher, puts a risk-based argument in a light tone, and is downloaded more than 8 million times.

—

The United States Supreme Court rules that greenhouse gases are pollutants, opening the door to litigation against industries producing high levels of carbon emissions.

—

The Carhullan Army, by Sarah Hall, a novel about a post-apocalyptic Britain whose ravages are largely due to environmental breakdown.

—

The Wild Places, by Robert Macfarlane.

—

A Moral Climate: The Ethics of Global Warming, by Michael Northcott, a philosophical/theological account of climate impacts.

—

UNESCO report: *Case Studies on Climate Change and World Heritage*.

—

The Cultures of Climate Change research group established at CRASSH, Cambridge University.

—

Weather Report: Art and Climate Change catalogue of the exhibition curated by Lucy Lippard in collaboration with EcoArts at the Boulder Museum of Contemporary Art in Colorado.

—

Ackroyd & Harvey realise *Flytower* on the exterior of London's National Theatre, growing grass on the north and west faces of the theatre's flytower.

—

Will Self's *The Book of Dave* imagines a future Britain reduced to an archipelago by rising seas.

2008

Voters in Ecuador approve a referendum on a new progressive constitution, which gives Nature the same rights as human beings.

—

Serious Things, by Gregory Norminton, a novel

featuring a reclusive climate scientist on the north coast of Scotland.

—

Bipolar, collection of essays on polar regions edited by Kathryn Yusoff.

—

Future Ethics symposium, University of Manchester.

—

The London Mayor's Green Theatre — Taking Action on Climate Change programme launched, aiming to reduce by 60% the energy used by London theatres by 2025.

—

Burn Up, a thriller about the oil industry and climate change written by Simon Beaufoy, broadcast on BBC2.

—

Six Greenpeace climate change activists cleared of causing £30,000 of criminal damage at Kingsnorth coal-fired power station. The activists admitted trying to shut down the station by occupying the smokestack in 2007, but argued that they were legally justified because they were trying to prevent climate change causing greater damage to property around the world. It was the first case in which preventing property damage caused by climate change had been used as part of a 'lawful excuse' defence.

—

Asia-Europe Dialogue on Arts, Culture & Climate Change in Beijing, China gathered 43 Asian and European artists, designers, architects, cultural practitioners, environmentalists and scientists, who participated in a three-day workshop.

—

Don DeLillo, Sarah Ruhl, José Rivera, Lisa Kron and Jon Robin Baitz are among the writers of nine short plays on the theme of global warming performed at Climate of Concern, the second annual New York University Humanities Festival organised by Lawrence Weschler.

—

Jeanette Winterson's cyclically plotted The Stone Gods imagines us repeating our ecological mistakes in the past and the future.

—

Alan Weisman's The World Without Us describes how, and how quickly, nature would begin to erode man-made structures and infrastructures.

—

The Carbon Diaries 2015, by Saci Lloyd — a young adult novel set in a Britain of the near future where carbon rationing has been implemented.

—

The Anthropocene, the 'age of humans', is proposed to the International Commission on Stratigraphy and the International Union of Geological Sciences as a formal unit of geological epoch division, recognising the extent of human impact on the Earth's ecosystems. The term was first used in print by Eugene Stormer and Paul Crutzen in 2000.

—

Centre for Sustainable Fashion established at the London College of Fashion by Dilys Williams.

—

The Climate Change Act 2008 is agreed, an Act of the Parliament of the United Kingdom to ensure that the net UK carbon account for all six Kyoto greenhouse gases is at least 80% lower than the 1990 baseline, by 2050. The Act aims to enable the UK to become a low-carbon economy.

2009

'Climategate': the web publication of hacked emails written by climate scientists fuels scepticism.

—

Level of CO_2 in the atmosphere reaches 385 ppm.

—

Mean global temperature (five-year average) is 14.5 °C, the warmest in hundreds, and probably thousands, of years.

—

One billion people take part in Earth Hour by switching off their lights at 8.30pm to mark the beginning of UN Climate Panel's meetings.

—

Major exhibitions on climate change and the arts: C Words, PLATFORM (Arnolfini, Bristol); RETHINK (Copenhagen); eARTh: Art of a Changing World (Royal Academy of Art, London); Radical Nature (Barbican, London); FutureSonic (Manchester); Climate for Change, (Liverpool); Two Degrees (ArtsAdmin, London).

—

Earth Matters on Stage, a symposium on theatre and ecology, and the Ecodrama Playwrights Festival are hosted by the University of Oregon.

—

The Contingency Plan by Steve Waters, the first play on climate change at a high-profile London theatre (Bush Theatre, London).

—

The United Nations Climate Change Conference, COP15, is held in Copenhagen, with no binding agreement reached.

—

Avatar: a film set in the mid-22nd century: mining on the planet of Pandora threatens the continued existence of a local tribe.

—

The Age of Stupid: a film directed by Franny Armstrong.

—

The LightSwitch Project, a play (also broadcast in 2011) commissioned by TippingPoint.

—

No Condition is Permanent: 19 Poets on Climate Justice and Change (PLATFORM).

—

Launch of 10:10, an organisation encouraging people, schools, businesses and organisations to cut their carbon consumption by 10% each year.

—

The first ArtsAdmin Two Degrees Festival, a biennial festival 'between art and action', London.

2010

Solar by Ian McEwan, a satirical novel focusing on climate change.

—

Long Horizons: An Exploration of Art and Climate Change, a collection of essays published by the British Council and Julie's Bicycle.

—

In-Flight Entertainment by Helen Simpson, a collection of climate change short stories.

—

Uncivilisation, the first Dark Mountain Festival.

—

Third Ring Out: Rehearsing the Future, an immersive performance by Metis Arts.

—

Earthquakes in London, a play by Mike Bartlett (National Theatre, London).

—

Floods in the Indus river basin of Pakistan cover one-fifth of the country's total land area and affect 20 million people.

—

Trashcatchers' Carnival, a TippingPoint commission, parades through Tooting in London.

—

The Jellyfish Theatre, a temporary structure built of reclaimed materials, opens in London with two plays on ecological themes: *Oikos* and *Protozoa*.

—

WWF publishes *Common Cause: The Case for Working with our Cultural Values*, showing the importance of values and goals in motivating change.

—

The US National Science Foundation awards a $700,000 grant to The Civilians, a New York theatre company, to finance *The Great Immensity*, a production about climate change.

—

Freedom by Jonathan Franzen, a 'green American novel', touches on mountaintop removal mining, species decline, habitat conservation, population control and suburban sprawl.

—

Commute of the Species uses puppets to chronicle the arrival of invasive animal and plant species in the Hudson River Valley while travelling on a Harlem line train from Grand Central station, New York.

The Department for Culture, Media and Sport in the UK publishes a Climate Change Plan.

—

The Cape Farewell exhibition *Unfold*, presenting the work of 25 artists who participated in expeditions to the High Arctic and to the Andes, opens at Kings Place, London, before touring nationally and internationally.

—

SHIFT, eight-day music-led festival, presented by Cape Farewell and Southbank Centre, London.

—

A catastrophic earthquake in Haiti kills an estimated 100,000–159,000 people and destroys vital infrastructure.

—

Earthquake in Chile of a magnitude of 8.8, caused damage to many cities.

—

The eruption of the Eyjafjallajökull volcano creates an ash cloud that grounds planes and affects activities in Europe and across the world.

—

Millions of barrels of oil pollute the Gulf of Mexico as a result of the Deepwater Horizon oil spill.

2011

Greenland, a play by Moira Buffini, Matt Charman, Penelope Skinner and Jack Thorne (National Theatre, London).

—

The Heretic, a play by Richard Bean (Royal Court Theatre, London).

—

Vendage Tardive, poems by Peter Reading.

—

100 Places to Remember Before they Disappear: photographs from 100 places around the world at risk of disappearing or seriously threatened by climate change.

—

The Ground Aslant: An Anthology of Radical Landscape Poetry edited by Harriet Tarlo.

—

Cave of Forgotten Dreams, a film about the Lascaux caves, directed by Werner Herzog.

—

High Arctic exhibition at the National Maritime Museum in collaboration with UVA and Cape Farewell, with poems by Nick Drake.

—

TippingPoint commissions: *As the World Tipped* by Wired Aerial Theatre; *Unplugged* by Tim Sutton; and *Funeral for Lost Species* by Feral Theatre.

—

Cape Farewell's Sea Change programme is launched.

—

After an earthquake and tsunami in Japan, the damaged Fukushima nuclear power plant releases radiation.

—

World human population reaches 7 billion.

—

A series of destructive tornados strike the United States, killing hundreds of people.

—

Publication of *Culture & Climate Change: Recordings*.

2012

Hurricane Sandy devastates the eastern third of North America, from Florida to Quebec, and from Michigan to Nova Scotia, as the largest Atlantic basin hurricane in history.
—
Attribution studies find recent disastrous heat waves, droughts, extremes of precipitation, and floods were made worse by global warming.
—
Flight Behaviour by Barbara Kingsolver explores one woman's encounter with climate science after she discovers the extraordinary natural spectacle of roosting Monarch butterflies.
—
The Walk From The Garden, an opera by Jonathan Dove, meditates on ecological apocalypse through the biblical story of Adam and Eve (Salisbury International Arts Festival).
—
Ten Billion by scientist Stephen Emmott and director Katie Mitchell: a new kind of scientific lecture-play (Royal Court Theatre).
—
The Kingsnorth Six, a docu-drama for BBC Radio 4 by Julia Hollander about Greenpeace activists who broke into Kingsnorth Power station in a protest against proposals to build new coal-fired power stations (see 2008 entry).
—

La cinquième saison (dir. Peter Brosens, Jessica Woodworth) — a film about a Belgian village in which, inexplicably, winter does not give way to spring, and nature becomes infertile; as a consequence human relationships deteriorate.
—
The Book of Barely Imagined Beings: A 21st Century Bestiary by Caspar Henderson.

2013

CO_2 concentrations in the atmosphere of 400 parts per million are recorded for the first time at the Mauna Loa Observatory in Hawaii.
—
November 8, 2013, super typhoon Haiyan ravages the central Philippines with a record-setting wind-speed at landfall of 195 miles per hour (314 km/h).
—
The IPCC publishes the first element of its Fifth Assessment Report (Working Group 1: The Physical Science Basis) concluding: 'Human influence on the climate system is clear. This is evident from the increasing greenhouse gas concentrations in the atmosphere, positive radiative forcing, observed warming, and understanding of the climate system.'
—
Shackleton's Man goes South, a novel by Tony White, published by the

Science Museum as their 2013 Atmosphere commission.
—
EU names 2013 the 'Year of Air'.
—
Client Earth environmental lawyers call on the European court to take action against the UK government over its failure to meet air quality standards. European Commission launches legal action against the UK in February 2014.

2014

Reports by working Group 2 (Impacts, Adaptation and Vulnerability) and 3 (Mitigation of Climate Change) of the IPCC are published, further consolidating and extending these massive reviews of peer-reviewed research related to climate change. WG2 summarises 'pervasive risks' but finds that opportunities still exist for effective responses. But it also finds that these responses will face challenges with higher levels of warming. WG3 finds that global emissions are accelerating despite reduction efforts, yet many pathways to emissions reductions are available.
—
2014 opens with experiences of extreme weather around the world, prompting renewed media and political interest in climate change.

The timeline is based on the one published in *Culture and Climate Change: Recordings* with some 60 additional entries. Two corrections have been made to the entry for the Great Smog in London: the date (1952 not 1953) and the figure given for premature deaths in early December due to the smog (from 1,000 to 4,000). A more comprehensive timeline, as well as pdfs of both books in this series, other resources produced by the Mediating Change group and news of events are available at: www.open.ac.uk/researchcentres/osrc/research/themes/mediating-change. To keep in touch with this work, to add items or offer comments on the timeline please email joe.smith@open.ac.uk with 'Timeline' in the subject.